D1097416

GLACIERS

By ROBERT P. SHARP
Chairman, Division of Geological Sciences
California Institute of Technology
Pasadena, California

Tenth Printing

CONDON LECTURES
OREGON STATE SYSTEM OF HIGHER EDUCATION
Eugene, Oregon—1960

PREFACE

Strict orthodoxy has not been adhered to in the format of this publication. There is no List of Illustrations because there are full captions to each and to have given a brief title would have meant using a statement without real significance for the sake of form. The Glossary appears before the text rather than after as is conventional. Since a glossary provides an explanation of words for those readers who may not be familiar with technical terms, it seemed to us that the best place to put it was before the text so the reader who needed it could familiarize himself with the terms in the proper order, so to speak, before turning to the text. Others may skip it.

Dr. Sharp in these lectures took his audiences over the surfaces of his "streams of ice," down into crevasses and into depths explored by scientific instruments and methods. Occasionally he took us on short jaunts to Greenland and Antarctica. He succeeded superbly in creating an understanding of and conveying a feeling for these glaciers with which he is on such familiar terms, in their beauty, their tremendous power, their complex structure and behavior whether in terms of masses of ice or component crystals, and showed how glaciers may be studied as ongoing illustrations of the geological processes at work in rocks throughout the long period of geologic time.

L. S. CRESSMAN, Chairman
Condon Lectures Committee

ACKNOWLEDGMENT

My indebtedness to the Condon Lecture Committee and to those associated with its function is great. Not only have they provided occasions on which to speak about glaciers to highly appreciative audiences, but they have furnished opportunity, one might even say forced me, to set down some of these matters on paper.

Delightful hospitality was extended on all sides, and the contact with the people of Oregon was pleasant, stimulating and educational. The State has done a good thing in establishing the Condon Lectureship, and its citizens can take pride in this function. Professor Donald B. Lawrence, the lecturer originally scheduled for 1960, could not participate owing to unfortunate illness, and it is proper that he be saluted here with warm hopes for a rapid recovery. The discerning reader will quickly realize that I am indebted to a host of able field associates and scientific colleagues who have participated in these researches. Many of their names do or will appear in scientific bibliographies on glaciers, along with other investigators upon whose work I have drawn without the recognition usually accorded by specific citation. Photographs borrowed from other are acknowledged individually.

Purposely, I refrain from naming individuals in this acknowledgment. Those to whom these words of warm appreciation are directed will recognize that fact. However, I cannot say "thank you" properly without turning specifically to Dr. L. S. Cressman, Chairman of the Condon Lecture Committee. He and his fellow committee members do a superb job.

TABLE OF CONTENTS

GLOSSARY OF TERMS

Efforts have been made to keep technical terms at a minimum in the following pages, but it is difficult to talk about science without using a few scientific words, just as it is hard to handle a foreign language without using some foreign words. The following notes are explanations rather than rigorous definitions.

Ablation refers to the wastage of glaciers, principally by melting and evaporation.

Albedo is a measure of the "reflectivity" of a surafce. An albedo of 60 for snow means that it reflects 60 per cent of the incoming radiation.

Anticline is a geological term used to describe an arched structure or fold within a layered or laminated rock in which the layers slope away from each other.

Axis of a fold, in very simplest terms, is the central line of the fold as it appears on the ground or on a map.

Bastion as used here refers to a large massive outcrop of rock that projects forward from its immediate surroundings, in this case ice or a valley wall.

Breccia is a geological deposit consisting of larger angular fragments usually embedded in finer material.

Calorie is a unit used to measure heat. It is the amount of heat required to raise the temperature of 1 gram of water 1° C.

Calving is the process of breaking away of blocks of ice from the margins of a glacier or ice barrier. This usually occurs where the glacier ends in a body of water. It also applies to breaking away of blocks from the walls of a crevasse.

Capillarity refers to the movement of a liquid, in this instance water, into small openings because of the attraction between the liquid and the walls of the opening.

Centigrade, a temperature scale commonly used in science on which the freezing point of pure water is 0° and the boiling point is 100°. Degrees centigrade can be converted to degrees Fahrenheit by multiplying by 1.8 and adding 32 (Example: 100° C $\times$ 1.8 = 180 + 32 = 212°, the boiling point of water on the Fahrenheit scale).

Component as used herein simply refers to the fraction of a displacement or movement that is parallel to any specified plane or direction.

Crevasse, an open linear crack in a glacier, the walls of which have separated so they are not uncommonly many feet apart.

Compressive flow, a type of flow that occurs in glaciers in reaches where the velocity is decreasing. The ice is not elastically compressed, but the body of the glacier is shortened and thickened.

Crystal lattice refers to the definite periodic arrangement of atoms in a solid crystalline substance.

Crystallographic plane is a specified plane that has a definite orientation with respect to the atomic structure of a crystal. Actually, there is an infinite number of planes with this orientation; it is the orientation rather than the individual plane that is important.

Crystallographic axis is a line which has a specified orientation with respect to the atomic structure of a crystal.

Cubic centimeter, a unit of volume in the metric system. One cubic inch equals 16.4 cubic centimeters.

Density is the mass (or weight) of a specified volume of substance, usually expressed in grams per cubic centimeter.

Diagenesis embodies the changes taking place in a sediment between the time of accumulation and complete solidification. Here they include the changes occurring in the transition between snow and glacier ice.

Dip is a geological term used to indicate in degrees how much an inclined plane diverges from horizontal.

Discharge as used herein refers to the total volume of ice passing through a specified cross section of a glacier in a specified unit of time.

Drag fold is a fold, usually of small size, formed in a layered or laminated mass where it has been locally distorted by displacement along a fracture. The layers appear to be bent by being dragged along the fracture surface.

Extending flow occurs in those parts of a glacier where the velocity is increasing. The ice is extended and thinned by this type of flow.

Facies is a term used by geologists, among others, to designate a lateral change in physical, chemical, or organic character of a rock formation.

Firn is a permeable aggregate of small grains of ice with a density greater than 0.55.

Firn limit is the lower edge of the annual snow blanket on a glacier at the end of the melting season.

Fold, in geological terms, is a bend in any planar feature such as a stratum or layer.

Glacier ice is a consolidated, relatively impermeable aggregate of ice crystals with a density greater than 0.84.

Gram, a unit of weight (mass) in the metric system. One ounce equals about 28 grams and one pound equals about 454 grams.

Icefall is an abnormally steep reach in a glacier's course down which ice flows with such high velocity that it is badly crevassed.

Metamorphism in the geological sense refers to changes in the minerals, grain size, and to some degree the chemistry of rock bodies subjected to deformation, heat, pressure, or circulating solutions in the earth's crust.

Moraine refers to rock debris piled up along the lateral or terminal parts of a glacier or laid down beneath it, as well as to the accumulations of rock debris on its surface marking the trace of septa of dirty ice.

Newtonian fluid is one that yields to increasing stress (force) at a uniformly increasing rate.

Ogives are features formed on or within glaciers below some icefalls. They consist either of a series of subequally spaced swells and swales on the ice surface or alternating arc-shaped bands of darker and lighter ice within the glacier.

Optical orientation refers to the orientation a crystal has with respect to the passage of light rays through it.

Outcrop is an exposure on the earth's surface of a rock unit or structure constituting a part of the earth's crust.

Perfectly plastic solid is one that yields only after a certain threshold value of stress has been exceeded and which theoretically yields at a infinite rate thereafter.

Phase as used here refers to the physical state of matter, for example, the solid, liquid and vapor phases of a substance.

Reach is an interval along a stream or a glacier which is distinguished by characteristics such as slope, width or depth, which makes it different from the reaches immediately above and below.

Septum as used herein refers to a more or less vertical partition of finite thickness between two ice streams or currents.

Shear is analogous to causing two cards in a deck to slip past one another.

Strain is the change in dimension or shape of a body when acted upon by deforming forces.

Stress in technical parlance is the force per unit area. It can be thought of as the force that causes deformation.

Sublimation is the transition of a substance directly from the solid to the vapor state.

Valley glacier is simply a stream of ice flowing down a valley as contrasted with a sheet of ice that spreads out over a featureless surface or is so thick that it completely buries the underlying topography.

INTRODUCTION

General Statement

Glaciers are one of the unusual, intriguing elements of our natural environment. Their influence on the world is much greater than one might expect considering that they currently cover only 10 per cent of the land and contain 3 per cent or less of the earth's water. No so long ago they covered nearly 30 per cent of the land and held an estimated 8 per cent of the water.

Our largest glaciers, the ice sheets of Greenland and Antarctica influence climatological environments of wide areas. Their state of health and their behavior are of world-wide interest because of the effect on sea level. As these glaciers grow and prosper, sea level falls, as they deteriorate and shrink, sea level rises. Changes in either direction can be embarrassing, if not downright disastrous, for man and his shoreline operations. Currently, some scientists are concerned that the increase of carbon dioxide in the atmosphere arising from industrial activity will cause a warming of the climate. They feel that in time this could lead to melting of these ice sheets and a disastrous rise of sea level. Actually, it is far from certain that a warmer climate will cause shrinkage of either the Greenland or Antarctic sheets. Both regions are presently much colder than necessary to maintain glaciers, and perhaps they could undergo some warming without any adverse effect on the glaciers. Indeed, warming might cause the glaciers to expand by enabling air masses to carry more snow to them. We really don't know, and it is partly because questions like this remain unanswered that we study glaciers.

In truth, most of us work with glaciers because we find them a never-ending source of fascinating information and discovery. As an earth scientist, I find a glacier interesting because it is a geological agent that can be studied in action. By observation and measurement, by careful probing and questioning, we gain answers from glaciers as to how they are feeling, what they are doing now, and what they may do in the future. In many geological situations a crime has been committed, but the principal suspect can't be grilled because he's dead. In glaciers we have a suspect who is very much alive and even willing to talk if interrogated properly.

Glaciers are sensitive and dynamic. They move, and they respond in many different and subtle ways to changes in the environment. They carefully and conscientiously record the effects of various meteorological elements. In some instances they are better at this than man with all his sophisticated instruments. The Greenland Ice Sheet well knows what the climate in Greenland is now and what it was 1000 years ago, and it will gladly tell us if we just ask in the right way.

In themselves glaciers are beautiful and mysterious. By their actions they have helped create some of the most spectacular scenery of this earth. They have been larger and more numerous in the past, and there is scant reason for thinking that they won't repeat this performance sometime in the future. If we wish to inhabit our earth with maximum comfort and pleasure, we must understand its various natural elements. As glaciologists, we simply wish to understand these ice bodies for their own sake, knowing that as our understanding improves we will be better able to answer questions of more practical concern.

This little pamphlet is not an "all about" book. It cannot possibly tell everything that is known about glaciers, and it does not pretend to do so. It attempts to present a description of some basic facts as background for an understanding of certain facets of modern glaciological research. It is not an elementary handbook, but it does attempt to present material in an informal style with a minimum of technical jargon. The hope is that the layman will find something of interest herein, and that the specialist will not regard it as completely devoid of meat. Emphasis is purposely placed upon matters and subjects of personal study. Many phenomena, as for example the nature, magnitude and cause of glacier fluctuations which attract great popular interest, are largely untreated. For the sake of simplicity and readability rigorous documentation is avoided. A selected list of references at the end will serve to lead those interested farther into special topics.

The Blue, Saskatchewan, and Malaspina-Seward Glaciers

These three glaciers are used as examples of the various features and phenomena discussed because they are well known to me. The Malaspina is a piedmont glacier, the term indicating that it is a body of ice at the foot of the mountains (Plate 1, A). It is a sheet covering about 850 square miles on the low flat coastal plain of southern Alaska that is fed by ice streams pouring from the lofty St. Elias Range to the north. The principal feeder is the Seward Glacier which gathers chiefly in a large intermontane basin well back in the highest part of the range (Plate 1, B). This basin, roughly 35 miles long by 20 miles wide, lies at elevations between 5000 and 7000 feet. It is surrounded by lofty peaks including Mount St. Elias (18,008 feet) and Mount Logan (19,850 feet), the second highest and one of the most massive mountains of North America. (Plate 2, A).

A—Western margin of Malaspina Glacier, Alaska, a piedmont ice sheet with Mount St. Elias in background. (Air photo by U.S. Coast Guard, August, 1953).

Plate 1

B—Accumulation basin of upper Seward Glacier, Yukon Territory, as viewed toward southwest from northeast edge. Alaska-Canada border runs along skyline ridge through Mount Augusta (just right of the man) and Mount St. Elias (18,008) at right. August, 1948.

A—View northwestward across upper Seward Glacier to Mount Logan (19,850), second highest peak in North America. Glaciological research camp in foreground, June, 1949.

Plate 2

B—Looking westward up Saskatchewan Glacier from south wall. Folded pattern of sedimentary layering visible in central part of glacier. Note also marginal crevasses and central longitudinal (splaying) crevasses. (Photo by M. F. Meier, 24 August, 1952).

Saskatchewan Glacier is one of the principal outlet ice streams of the Columbia Ice Field on the boundary between Banff and Jasper national parks in the Canadian Rockies of Alberta. (Plate 2, B). The Saskatchewan has a geometrically simple ice tongue extending in a nearly straight channel of fairly uniform cross section roughly 5.5 miles below the firn edge. It has only one attached tributary.

The Blue is a small valley glacier draining from the northeast slope of Mount Olympus in the heart of the Olympic Peninsula of northwestern Washington (Plate 3, A). It is only 2.6 miles long but has a 1000-foot icefall and a high material turnover related to heavy winter snows and strong melting in summer. The easy accessibility and simple logistics make this an excellent laboratory for glaciological research, the use of which is graciously granted by the National Park Service.

Plate 3

A—Looking southwestward to Blue Glacier. Mount Olympus and accumulation area of Blue Glacier on skyline, icefall in upper middle, terminus out of view to lower right. (Photo by C. R. Allen, late August, 1958).

B—Small unnamed glacier west of Alsek River in St. Elias Mountains, Yukon Territory, Canada. Picture shows clearly the upper (white) accumulation area, the firn edge and the lower (darker) wastage area of a glacier. Photographed in late summer of 1951, an abnormally dry year.

THE CONSTITUENT PARTS OF A GLACIER

Accumulation and Wastage Areas

Most glaciers have two principal parts, an accumulation area and a wastage area (Plate 3, B ; and Fig. 1). The accumulation area comprises that part of the glacier in which the total snowfall exceeds the amount of melting during a year. In the wastage area melting exceeds snowfall. The two areas are separated by the annual snowline.

In winter, most glaciers are entirely covered by snow, but melting during summer causes the edge of the snow cover to recede gradually upglacier. Near the end of the melting season it reaches the highest position for the year. This is the annual snowline on the glacier, and it can be specifically identified in terms of a calendar year, for example the snowline of 1955. Glaciologists have chosen to call this the firn line because it is usually lower than and not continuous with the snowline on adjacent ground. In simplest terms, firn is old granular snow. The term firn limit is preferred by some because the edge of the snow is usually an irregular, frayed, patchy zone and not a line.

In many ways snowline is a better term than firn limit because the edge of the snow and the edge of the firn need not coincide. In an exceptionally warm, dry year the snowline can recede to an abnormally high position, exposing the edges of one or more older firn layers (Plate 4, A). Use of the term firn line or limit for the edge of the annual snow blanket in such a situation leads to confusion. For this reason, we shall

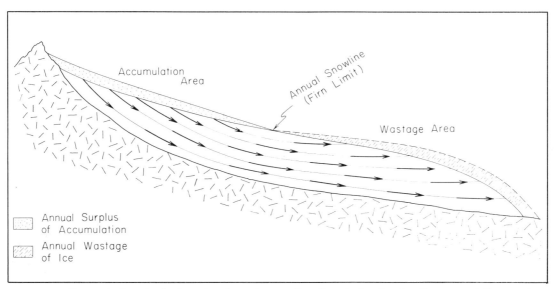

FIGURE 1. Longitudinal section through a small valley glacier showing the accumulation-wastage area relationship and the deduced longitudinal flowlines.

A—Looking northwestward onto surface of Humes Glacier in Olympic Mountains, Washington. Photo shows edges of at least 5 annual firn layers as exposed in late August, 1958, a warm dry year. White patch at left is 1957-58 snow.

Plate 4

B—Air view northeastward up the Barnard Glacier in the St. Elias Mountains of Alaska, August, 1949. A textbook example of a compound valley glacier fed by many tributary ice streams.

here use the term annual snowline for the upper limit attained by the edge of the annual snow blanket on the glacier. The term *firn edge* will be used for the edge of the firn mantle on the glacier.

One should realize that glacier movement is constantly carrying the firn edge downglacier. This advance of the firn edge is partly cancelled by a recession caused by melting, and over a period of time under uniform conditions a rough balance is attained. Nonetheless, on many glaciers the firn edge lies at a lower, more advanced position than the annual snowline except in years of exceptionally heavy accumulation. Therefore, an exposed firn edge below the annual snowline on the glacier does not mean that the year of observation is necessarily a poor one for the glacier. The snowline may well be at its normal position.

Ice Streams

Valley glaciers are like rivers of water in that most of any size have tributaries, each making its own contribution to the trunk stream. This is readily apparent in large compound valley glaciers, such as the Barnard of Alaska (Plate 4, B) which may be fed by as many as 10 to 20 tributary ice streams. However, there is an important difference from rivers in that the individual streams of ice do not intermix. Each maintains its integrity and individuality. An ice stream may become greatly thinned by compression and extension, but it does not mix with its neighbors. This difference is due to the fact that the flow of water in rivers is turbulent, while the flow of ice is not. However, streams of ice can adapt themselves nicely to the major configurations of their valleys as is beautifully shown by the Kaskawulsh Glacier (Plate 5, A).

A compound valley glacier is composed of individual streams of ice lying side by side and, in most instances, extending from the surface of the floor. We know, however, that some ice streams do not extend to the floor because they do not reach the glacier's terminus. They are destroyed by melting somewhere above the terminus, as shown by the fact that the marginal moraines curve around and join to form a transverse loop (Plate 5, B). These ice streams must have occupied an inset position (Fig. 2). They usually represent smaller tributaries that descended from high-level hanging valleys or lacked the volume and punch to take up a side-by-side position with other streams in the trunk glacier. In effect they have ridden down the valley on the backs of the other ice streams which continue to the terminus.

Icefalls

Just as rivers have waterfalls, glaciers have icefalls (Plate 7, A). Both mark abnormally steep reaches in the channel of flow. There is a distinct difference, however, in that a waterfall produces a free fall of

Plate 5

A—Looking up the Kaskawulsh Glacier in the St. Elias Mountains, Yukon Territory, Canada, in late August, 1951.

B—View westward to upper Muldrow Glacier and Mt. McKinley, Alaska. Note the transverse morainal loop on the ice surface at the right side of the glacier in lower central part of the photograph, suggesting an inset ice stream relationship. This glacier experienced a sudden surge of rapid movement during the winter of 1956-57 accompanied by pronounced lowering of the ice level in upper reaches. (Air photo by Bradford Washburn).

water, but free fall of ice occurs only to a limited degree. An icefall involves greatly accelerated flow down an abnormally steep slope. The increased velocity greatly thins the ice by extension (stretching) and gives rise to numerous crevasses. Little is known about the velocity of flow over icefalls, but it has been measured at about ten feet per day

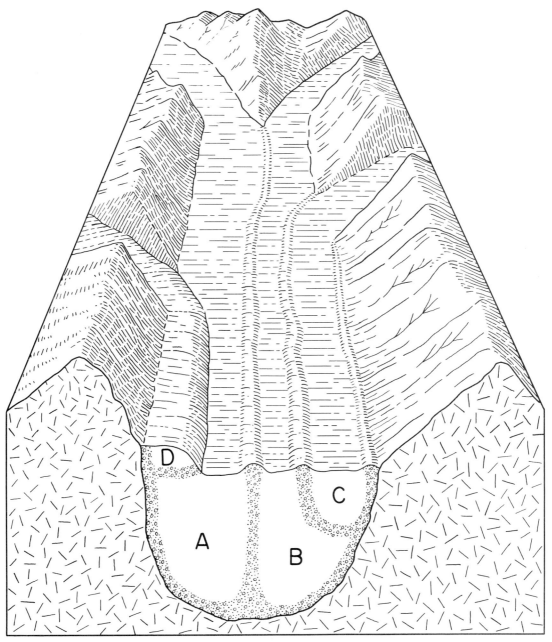

FIGURE 2. Cross-section sketch of a valley glacier consisting of ice streams in the side-by-side (A and B), inset (C), and superimposed (D) positions.

in one instance and may perhaps attain several tens of feet per day in the largest icefalls. The masses of ice between crevasses are badly fractured so that large blocks frequently break off and tumble into the crevasses on either side, partly filling them with broken brecciated debris. This constitutes about the only true falling that occurs within an icefall, but because of it and associated avalanches, icefalls tend to be noisy, at least in summer. Owing to the great amount of crevassing large icefalls usually present an over-all appearance of impenetrable chaos.

The height and width of an icefall is purely a function of the underlying bedrock channel and the size of the glacier. Most are a few hundred to 1500 feet high, but some attain a height of 3000 feet or more. Icefalls usually occupy the entire width of the glacier, but a compound valley glacier can be made up of ice streams some of which have passed over icefalls and others of which have not. Among other things, icefalls are important for the structures they create within glaciers.

THE GLACIER BUDGET

The Budget Year

Just like our national government each glacier operates on a budget and has a budget year which is not the calendar year. However, the budget year of a glacier is not always of the same duration, and it does not start and terminate on the same dates each year. It is easy enough to define what constitutes the beginning and end of a budget year, but determination of these limits in the field is more difficult. The end of a budget year can be defined as that time in the fall at which the accumulation of new snow exceeds the wastage of older material. On a time-plot of accumulation and wastage, the budget year ends when the line of accumulation rises above the line of wastage, the intersection marking the exact date of the termination, see point A in Figure 3. The new budget year extends to a similar occurrence the next fall, although during the interim the line of accumulation has necessarily fallen below the line of wastage. The intersection made during this descent (see point W, in Fig. 3) marks the beginning of the wastage season. This is the season during which total wastage exceeds total accumulation. Some investigators consider that a new budget year begins when accumulation exceeds wastage at the firn limit (annual snowline).

Income and Expenditure

Like the government, the items on the glacier's budget are those of income and expenditure, and like the government, it strives to maintain

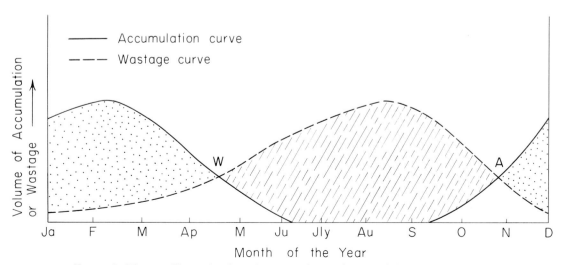

FIGURE 3. Diagram illustrating how the curves for total accumulation and total wastage as plotted against time can be used to define a budget year. Intersection at A marks beginning of the budget year, and intersection at W defines the beginning of the wastage season. If stippled area equals crosslined area, glacier's budget is balanced.

a balanced budget. In fact, it is usually more successful, especially in dealing with deficits. If a deficit occurs, the glacier contracts in order to decrease expenditures. If the glacier experiences a surplus, it promptly expands in order to dispose of this additional income. It abhors both surplus and deficit, and does its level best to live exactly up to its income. Glaciers that have over-expanded during periods of prosperity sometimes stagnate during the following "depression" (Plate 6, A, B).

In keeping a glacier's budget, it would be best to record the gross (total) income and gross expenditures following the normal practice in business accounting. Unfortunately, this is difficult as it requires year-round observation at many different points. The usual practice is to record net income and net expenditures. The first is determined by measuring the volume of snow remaining above the annual snowline at the end of the melting season. This can be done by digging pits or boring core holes at numerous locations in the accumulation area and measuring the thickness and density of the residual snow layer. This layer is roughly wedge-shaped, increasing from a thin edge at the snowline to maximum thickness near the glacier's head. The net expenditure is determined by measuring the wastage of older materials, ice and firn, below the snowline. This is usually done with reference to stakes, set in holes bored deeply into the firn and ice, on which the level of the surface has been marked at various times of the year. Measurement of ablation requires a more extended series of observations and in general is more difficult and less accurate than measurement of accumulation. If the glacier terminates in a water body, calving of bergs is a further complication.

To facilitate comparison, the figures on net income and net wastage are usually recalculated into equivalent volumes of water, the densities of the original materials being different. These items can then be recorded in normal balance-sheet manner, or they can be plotted on a chart. A useful practice in instances where gross income and expenditures are known is to plot them in terms of altitude on the glacier (Fig. 4). This permits one to determine at a glance the location of the principal areas of surplus and deficit, and to some degree the plot reflects the shape of the glacier.

The Budget Balance

In any single year, it is unlikely that the items of income and expenditure exactly balance. However, if the glacier is adjusted to its environment, they come close to a balance over a period of time probably not exceeding 5 to 10 years for small glaciers. The accumulation area is the nourishment zone of the glacier. The excess of material accumulated there must be transported to the wastage area where it is expended. Thus, a glacier is in the business of transportation, and the build up of a surplus in the accumulation area year after year is the basic cause of movement.

Studies of the glacier budget are a more satisfactory way of evaluating the health of a glacier than observations of fluctuations in its terminal position. For one thing, the budget figures are current and give a measure of conditions during the year of observation. Fluctuations of the terminus reflect individual eccentricities of glacier behavior or events that may have occurred some unknown time in the past. Budget studies also give a more truly quantitative measure of the changes involved. They are definitely more trouble to make, but the results well justify the time and effort.

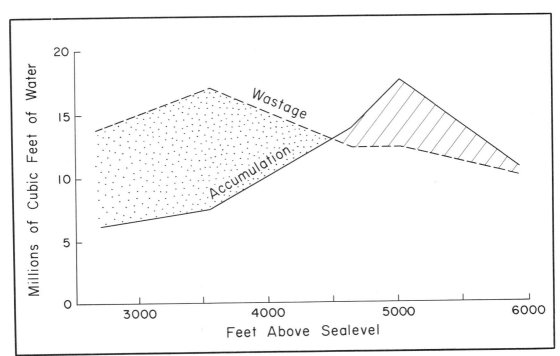

FIGURE 4. Variation in accumulation and wastage with altitude; essentially a régime diagram as modified from Ahlmann. Increments of area included between increments of altitude are not equal, so shape of curve reflects areal form of glacier. A quick estimate of material balance can be obtained by comparison of the crosslined (net accumulation) and stippled (net wastage) areas on the diagram. In the instance shown wastage exceeds accumulation and the régime is negative.

Plate 6

A—Looking down onto stagnant ice of lower Wolf Creek (or Steele) Glacier in St. Elias Mountains, Yukon Territory, July, 1941).

B—Stagnant ice (black cliff) at southeast margin of Malaspina Glacier, Alaska. Alder thickets growing in 12-16 inch cover of sandy gravel on the ice surface. Nearby, 100-year-old spruce trees grow in 20-30 inch mantle of superglacial debris on ice. July, 1949.

A—Looking southwestward up the Blue Glacier in the Olympic Mountains, Washington, to the 1000-foot icefall. Universal stage for measurement of ice crystal orientation in the foreground. August, 1957.

Plate 7

B—Measuring the warming up of the winter's chilled layer on a temperate glacier, upper Seward Glacier, Alaska, June, 1949.

GLACIERS AND CLIMATE

Glacio-Meteorology

Glaciers are a progeny of climate. They are utterly dependent upon elements of the climatic environment for birth and for sustaining life. The size to which a glacier grows, its state of health, its degree of activity, its life span and history are all controlled or strongly influenced by meteorological factors. The relationships are not as simple as might appear at first glance, and a special discipline known as glacio-meteorology has grown up to deal with them. The presentation made here is over-simplified, but the aspects of this field are too varied and complex to be treated more comprehensively. It is important that glacio-meteorological studies advance at a rapid pace. Since glaciers are delicately adjusted to the climatic environment, they are in a sense competent and sensitive observers and recorders of climate. If we hope to read this record, both current and ancient, we must understand how glaciers respond to changes in the various meteorological factors. The same information will enable us to predict what glaciers are likely to do as the climate changes in the future.

Accumulation and wastage (ablation) are the principal subjects with which glacio-meteorology deals. Accumulation is the life blood of a glacier, and wastage determines the amount and rate at which its resources are spent. Accumulation on most glaciers occurs in the form of snow. Hoar frost, refrozen meltwater, and such sources of substance are only locally important. By and large, it is clear that thrift is as great a virtue among glaciers as it is among human beings. The preserving of snow once it has been received can be more important to glacier health than the total amount of snow that falls. This is well demonstrated by the fact that the world's largest glaciers, the ice sheets of Greenland and Antarctica, occupy areas of extremely low precipitation. They are big because they are exceedingly thrifty. For this reason, and because the factors controlling the amount of snow falling in an area are relatively straightforward, glacio-meteorologists tend to focus on matters affecting wastage.

Melting

The principal means of wastage attributable to meteorological factors is melting. The causes of melting include radiation, both direct and indirect, conduction which is aided by convection and turbulence, and condensation. Matters such as cloud cover, humidity, wind and the physical properties of the wasting material, especially its albedo (reflectivity), are important indirect influences that cannot be ignored.

It has become painfully apparent from studies to date that extrapolations from one area to another or from one time to another are frightfully uncertain. For example, the relative role of direct radiation from the sun as a cause of melting changes with the season, the time of day, the latitude, the altitude, the cloud cover, the direction of exposure, the humidity, the albedo of the material and possibly still other factors. In some areas direct radiation accounts for more than 80 per cent of the total wastage, in others only 8 per cent. On the average over the period 1930-39, in June on Kårsa Glacier in Sweden direct radiation caused 75 per cent of the wastage of snow, in August only 30 per cent. The relative effectiveness of direct radiation generally increases with altitude owing to clearer air and lower air temperature. It may also increase with latitude although the lower angle of incidence of the rays and increasing cloudiness exert an opposite effect that at times can dominate. Radiation even undergoes a diurnal variation in its effects because of the changing angle of incidence and variations in albedo. Indirect radiation shows variations of similar magnitude, but they are not necessarily in the same phase or controlled by the same factors.

The point is simply this. Radiation is clearly one of the major factors in the wastage of glaciers, yet it varies over a wide range for a host of causes. Its role in the wastage of a specific glacier must be studied firsthand. Conclusions based on prior experience in other areas, even though sound in principle, are likely to lead to errors if applied without local study because of complex relationships between the many variables.

Much the same thing can be said for the other meteorological factors of wastage. Conduction of heat from the atmosphere is certainly capable of melting ice, and the temperature of the air is clearly all-important. It is perhaps less obvious that wind exerts a major effect on melting by conduction. Without the turbulence resulting from atmospheric movements, a thin layer of air next to the ice or snow is rapidly chilled to 0° C. Until the chilled layer is removed, melting by conduction practically comes to a standstill, and it is for this reason that wind is so important. It is more effective than convection in removing the cold air and in bringing a new supply of warm air into contact with the ice.

The moisture content of the air is also significant, for moist air has a greater specific heat than dry air at the same temperature. But moist air can be even more effective as a melting agent in another way. If the moisture content (relative humidity) is great enough so that the air reaches the dew point as it is cooled in contact with the ice or snow, condensation occurs. Condensation of water vapor at 0° C. results in a large evolution of heat, nearly 600 calories per gram of water. This is sufficient to melt about 7½ grams of ice or snow, assuming the material was close to the freezing point. Condensation of vapor is thus an effective mechanism of melting, and the process is promoted by wind action.

One is usually inclined to think that rain would melt considerable snow and ice. This feeling is probably based partly on intuition and partly on casual observation. However, the few studies made to date suggest that rain is not a major factor in the wastage of most glaciers. In part this is due to the fact that the temperature of much rain water is not far above freezing so the supply of heat available is small. One inch of rain at a temperature of 10° C. (50° F.) has a heat content sufficient to melt only ⅛ inch of ice. Perhaps, rain gives the impression of being more effective in melting snow than it actually is because of the compaction and settling it causes.

Evaporation

At this point, it would perhaps be well to pay brief respects to the overrated role of evaporation (or sublimation) in the wastage of most ice and snow. To begin with, evaporation of ice is a costly process in terms of energy (heat). Close to 680 calories are needed to evaporate one gram of ice compared to 80 calories required to melt the same ice. In terms of heat requirements evaporation is manifestly a grossly inefficient way of wasting ice. However, nature does not always do things in the best or most efficient way, and perhaps she just can't help indulging in some evaporation even though she knows she really shouldn't. There is some validity to this point, but probably not much.

Evaporation occurs chiefly when the relative humidity is so low that air in contact with ice does not reach the dew point as it is cooled to 0° C. This condition exists chiefly in winter when the air is cold and dry. Even under these conditions evaporation must be limited in absolute terms because the amount of moisture that can be taken up by cold air is small and the available energy is at a minimum. Many statements have been made on the basis of general field observations to the effect that much evaporation of snow occurs, especially at high altitude. With a few exceptions, actual measurements supporting such statements are lacking. Indeed one experiment designed expressly to demonstrate the importance of evaporation in the wasting of snow at high altitude succeeded in showing that evaporation was minor at best and indeed at times was outweighed by condensation. Be this as it may, glacio-meteorological studies in a number of different areas have shown that evaporation usually accounts for not more than 2 to 5 per cent of the total wastage of the glaciers being investigated. Even where evaporation may at times be the sole or dominant mode of wastage, as in Pearyland in far northern Greenland, the total amount of wastage is relatively small.

The Total Wastage

The following tabulation (*see* table 1, next page) shows the relative parts played in wastage of some specific glaciers by the three principal meterological factors, radiation, conduction, and condensation. The figures given are not exactly comparable as the time interval, season, and orographic settings are different in each instance. Nonetheless the comparisons are interesting and informative.

The Coupling of Glaciers to Climate

The effect of various glacio-meteorological factors is strongly dependent upon aspects of the local setting. In the instance of a small glacier, the local topography, the orientation and exposure, the relation to prevailing winds, the size, shape and location of the accumulation region and its area-distribution in terms of altitude all play a part in determining the glacier's response to climatic variations. This has been demonstrated repeatedly by the remarkably different behaviors displayed by closely adjacent valley glaciers. One glacier may recede while the other advances, although they are so close that it is difficult to see how the climatic conditions on them can be much different. Insofar as the glaciers are concerned the climate may be very different, and the glaciers themselves may react differently to the same climatic change. Appreciation of some aspects of this relationship can be gained by an inspection of Geiger's delightful little book "The Climate Near the Ground" in which he so effectively documents the great differences in temperature, wind and precipitation that exist over small areas. Thus, to attain an understanding of the coupling of a glacier to its climatic environment, one must know the glacio-meteorological factors involved, and he must also understand how each particular glacier reacts to those factors.

Glaciers as Weather Observers

In some ways a glacier is a better observer of weather than man. As Carl Benson remarks, the interior of the Greenland Ice Sheet, where wastage is practically nil, constitutes an infinite series of precipitation gauges. Benson effectively demonstrates that the ice sheet gives a far better measure of total annual precipitation than any of the artificial gauges of man in Greenland. Rain and snow gauges are notoriously inaccurate in areas of strong winds, such as parts of the Arctic and most of the Antarctic.

Table 1. Relative Roles of Radiation, Conduction-Convection and Condensation in Wastage of Ice or Snow on Various Glaciers as Modified from Orvig

Glacier (Year and Season)	Location (Lat. and Long.)	Elevation (feet)	Radiation %	Conduction and Convection %	Condensation %	Type of Material
Isachsen's Plateau (1934; 26 June-15 Aug.)	West Spitsbergen (79° 09' N., 12° 56' E.)	2650	56	29	15	Snow
Fourteenth of July Glacier (1934; 31 May-31 Aug.)	West Spitsbergen (79° 08' N., 12° E.)	575	47	53 including both		Ice
Sveanor (snow field) (1931; 30 June-6 Aug.)	North East Land Spitsbergen (79° 56' N., 18° 18' E.)	17	24	58	18	Snow
Fröya Glacier (1939; 1 Aug.-18 Aug.)	Northeast Greenland (74° 24' N., 20° 50' W.)	1486	8	83	9	Snow
Kårsa Glacier (1942-1948) ; August)	Swedish Lapland (68° 20' N., 18° 20' E.)	Above and below 3610	55 / 32	29 / 44	16 / 24	Ice / Snow
Hoffellsjökull (1936; April-October)	Iceland (64° 30' N., 15° 30' W.)	Below 3280	14	86 including both		Ice
Barnes Ice Cap (1950; 25 May-4 Aug.)	Baffin Island (69° 43' N., 72° 13' W.)	2850	68	32 including both		Mostly snow
Penny Ice Cap (1953; 13 July-26 July)	Baffin Island (66° 59' N., 65° 28' W.)	6725	61	30	9	Snow
Vernagtferner I (1950; 21 Aug.-31 Aug.)	Austrian Alps (46° 50' N., 10° 45' E.)	9755	81	15	4	Ice
Vernagtferner II (1952; 21 July-4 Aug.)	Austrian Alps (46° 50' N., 10° 45' E.)	9740	84	16 including both		Ice

In areas where the mean annual temperature is below freezing and essentially no melting occurs, the glaciers also maintain reliable records of mean annual temperature. All one has to do is dig down about 30 feet into the snow or firn and measure its temperature, regardless of the time of year. This value has been shown to depart less than 1° C. from the mean annual temperature. It is this technique that permitted the American party occupying the South Pole during the International Geophysical Year to announce within a few days after their arrival that the mean annual temperature at the pole is in the neighborhood of —60° F.

Warm Glaciers and Cold Glaciers

To those who have given no thought to the matter, it may seem a little silly to talk about the temperature of glaciers. After all, aren't all glaciers cold? This is true only in a relative sense. There are varying degrees of coldness, and the differences between glaciers at or close to the melting temperature and those at 10°, 20°, or 30° below 0° C. are profound. For these reasons, glaciologists like to speak of "warm" glaciers and "cold" glaciers. We shall shortly see what the basic differences are.

Climatological environment is, of course, the controlling influence in determining the temperature of a glacier. The number of factors involved is relatively large and their interrelations complex and not clearly understood. Such factors as air temperature, incoming and outgoing radiation, cloud cover, amount of snow, rain, wind, condensation, evaporation and melting all play a role in determining the temperature of a glacier.

There is no way to make a glacier cold, other than to build it up out of cold snow or chill it by outgoing radiation or conduction to the atmosphere. A glacier can be no colder than its environment, unless for some reason the environment has suddenly become warmer, and the glacier has not yet adjusted to the change.

Obviously, a glacier cannot be warmer than the melting temperature or it wouldn't exist, but are there glaciers at the melting temperature? Yes there are, and since most of the snow that makes up glaciers accumulates at temperatures below freezing, there must be some means of warming it to the melting point in such glaciers. One would expect that incoming radiation and conduction from a warm atmosphere could do the job, but these factors are effective only as long as the surface materials (snow, firn, ice) are below the freezing point. Radiation does not penetrate in significant quantities to a depth of more than a few inches, and once a surface layer of finite thickness has been raised to the melting temperature, conduction is no longer effective. This happens because the surface layer is at 0° C. throughout, no temperature gradient exists, and consequently no heat conduction can occur.

This bring us to an important point. The subsequent warming of the underlying material is accomplished mostly by the downward movement (percolation) of water from the surface. A little of this water may come from rain, but mostly it is derived from melting of snow through conduction and radiation at the surface. The water moves downward freely through the underlying pervious snow and firn. It produces only a little warming by conduction for it is at or close to 0° Cent., but it eventually refreezes in contact with the colder underlying materials. Each gram of water gives up 80 calories of heat as it changes to ice. This is sufficient to raise the temperature of 1 gram of ice by about 160° C., or 160 grams of ice by 1° C. Clearly then the refreezing of downward-percolating meltwater can be a major mechanism for warming up snow, firn and ice, and it is the basic cause for the existence of "warm" and "cold" glaciers.

Warm glaciers are those that at some time during the summer season attain the melting temperature throughout. In winter, warm glaciers develop a surficial crust a few tens of feet thick that is temporarily chilled below freezing by conduction and outgoing radiation. In summer, this chilled layer is brought back to the melting point largely by the refreezing of downward-percolating meltwater (Plate 7, B). The part of the glacier lying below this surficial zone of seasonal chilling remains constantly at the melting temperature and doesn't know the difference between summer and winter except for variations in the amount of meltwater that percolates down from above. This is why it is possible to bore holes into warm glaciers with thermal hotpoints without having the holes immediately closed by freezing. Once the ice in the hole is melted to water by the hotpoint, there is no residual supply of cold to reconvert it to ice.

A cold glacier is ideally one in which no surface melting occurs. Its temperature throughout is below freezing, and in places such as interior Greenland and the heart of Antarctica it is many tens of degrees below freezing. Some cold glaciers do experience a limited amount of surface melting, but it is never great enough to bring the entire body to the melting temperature.

Years ago the famed Swedish glaciologist, Hans W. Ahlmann, with commendable scientific intuition, recognized the significance of temperature differences in glaciers and proposed a classification into temperate (warm) and polar (cold) glaciers. This was a major contribution, but it had one inherent weakness. The description applies only to a local area on a glacier. A large glacier could be cold near its head and warm in its lower reaches.

A solution to this problem has recently been proposed by Carl Benson on the basis of studies of the snow and firn blanket on the Greenland Ice Sheet. Benson recognizes distinct physical and thermal differences in the snow-firn mantle which are dependent upon the development of meltwater. These differences lead to recognition of four zones within this surface mantle. Normally, a glacier will have two or three of these zones; only very large glaciers are likely to have all four. A classification of glaciers could easily be made on the number and kinds of zones. Since the zones are dependent upon the climatological environment, especially temperature, we, in effect, arrive at a classification of glaciers by temperature.

At this point, one may wish to ask about the possibilities of warming a glacier from its underside by conduction of heat from the warm interior of the earth. The average amount of heat conducted to the earth's surface is 38 calories per square centimeter per year. This is sufficient to melt about ¼ inch of ice per year. In a warm glacier the temperature gradient is such that this heat cannot be conducted surfaceward, and it must go to melting of the ice (Fig. 5). Thus, the internal temperature

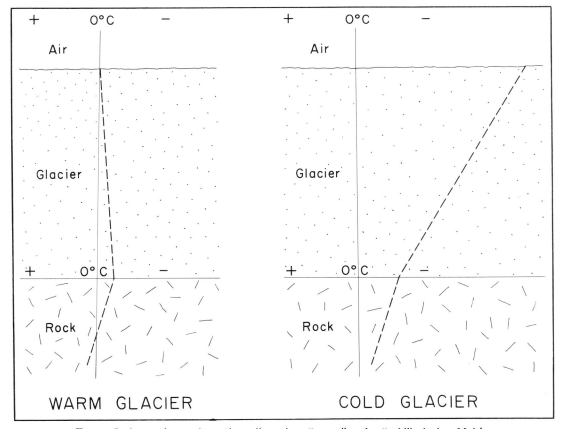

FIGURE 5. Approximate thermal gradients in a "warm" and a "cold" glacier. Melting must occur at base of warm glacier because earth's heat cannot be conducted through the ice on the reverse gradient (cold to warm) established by the pressure-melting temperature.

of a warm glacier is not affected by heat from within the earth. However, in a cold glacier the gradient can be suitable for conduction of this heat and it can be utilized to warm up the ice.

Over a long period of time an equilibrium can be established between the amount of heat coming to the base of the glacier and the amount being transferred to the atmosphere at its surface by conduction and outgoing radiation. Recent data from Antarctica suggest that such equilibrium conditions are attained only slowly, and they do not at present exist in some parts of the Antarctic Ice Sheet, a very cold glacier.

The temperature conditions of a glacier are important with respect to its physical characteristics and behaviors. Ice at or close to the melting point yields more readily to stress, so warm glaciers tend to deform more easily and flow more rapidly than cold glaciers. Warm ice also recrystallizes more quickly producing a considerable difference in textures and crystal orientation. The development of meltwater and its refreezing within the snow and firn aids in the conversion of snow to glacier ice and produces layers, lenses and vertical columnar masses of ice (Fig. 6) within the firn that are lacking on glaciers devoid of meltwater.

The temperature of a glacier is an important matter. Temperature strongly influences its behavior, the internal constitution and the structure. It further permits a classification that has genetic significance with respect to the climatological environment.

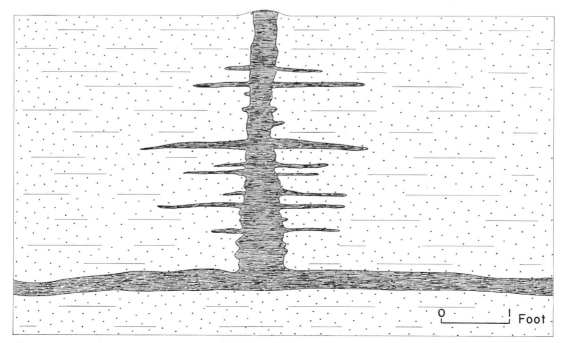

FIGURE 6. Field sketch of a pipe-like mass of ice with horizontal projections formed in firn of upper Seward Glacier by refreezing of downward percolating meltwater.

THE CONVERSION OF SNOW TO GLACIER ICE

Basic Relationships

Glaciers are made from snow. Each crystal of glacier ice represents hundreds to thousands of tiny snowflakes that have been welded together into a single homogeneous crystal structure. Many of the physical characteristics of glacier ice are, therefore, inherited from the parent material—snow. Knowledge of this parent material and of the processes and mechanisms converting it to solid ice contributes to our understanding of glaciers.

Initially, the parent material is a light, loose, fluffy aggregate of delicate snow flakes. It accumulates in successive layers, each layer representing a single storm or different phases within a storm (Plate 8, A). These layers display differences in density, grain size, porosity, permeability, hardness and compactness reflecting variations in the conditions of precipitation and deposition. The stratification is preserved for a considerable time and often exists in recognizable form far down into the ice tongue (Plates 2, B and 10, A). Some of the changes that occur during the conversion of snow to solid ice accentuate rather than weaken the layering.

Differences between the snow layers tell a good deal about the early history of the glacier materials. Since they entomb pollen, rock dust, volcanic ash, cosmic dust and other impurities, they also provide a record of earthly and cosmic events that makes interesting reading. Eventually, it may be possible to trace the history back for thousands of years by study and analysis of cores from deep drill holes in the large ice masses of Greenland and Antarctica.

The individual strata of the accumulated snow occur in groups that represent the deposits of single budget years. Such a group of strata is termed an annual layer (Plate 8, A). The recognition and proper identification of annual layers, sometimes easy sometimes difficult, is an important step in ascertaining the state of health of a glacier.

Snow to Firn to Glacier Ice

Snow begins to change in physical characteristics almost as soon as it comes to rest on the glacier surface. The beautiful, delicate skeleton crystals composing snow flakes are rapidly transformed by sublimation, local melting, crushing and compaction into small nearly spherical granules of solid ice. This change occurs within a few days or at most a few

A—Horizontal stratification of firn as exposed in crevasse wall of upper Seward Glacier, September, 1948. Dark, prominent layers mark top of annual sequences.

Plate 8

B—A glacially scoured and striated rock outcrop in the Trinity Alps, California.

weeks in all but the coldest environments. The resulting loose, highly pervious, granular aggregate is known as old snow, more in reference to its physical state than to its actual age. The corn snow of skiers is of this character. This transformation is accompanied by a marked increase in density, from less than 0.1 in the initial material to 0.3 or higher in old snow. As the alteration continues it produces larger grains, closer packing and increased density.

Densification proceeds smoothly and at a reasonably rapid rate to a value of about 0.55, at which point the rate and mechanism change abruptly. For years, glaciologists have made an arbitrary distinction between old snow and firn, although the gross physical aspects of the two are essentially the same. Both consist of loose, highly pervious aggregates of small, nearly spherical ice granules. Carl Benson and Don Anderson now propose that a density of 0.55 be taken as the separation point between old snow and firn. This makes sense since both the rate and mechanism of densification are different beyond this value. The density, 0.55, is apparently the greatest that can be attained in old snow simply by shifting the grains around so they fit most snugly together. Increases beyond that value involve modifications of the individual grains by deformation, local melting, refreezing, recrystallization and possibly other processes or mechanisms. These changes allow the grains to fit still more closely together reducing the pore space and permeability, and increasing density and compactness.

Eventually, the process reaches the stage where the remaining pore spaces are sealed off, and the mass becomes impermeable. This transformation occurs within a surprisingly narrow density range, between 0.82 and 0.84. Further reductions of pore space and increases in density continue up to values of 0.89 or 0.90, which are common for glacier ice. The ultimate limit of course is the density of pure ice, 0.917, but this is seldom attained except in individual crystals.

The Role of Meltwater

The nature and rate of processes converting snow to glacier ice change with the climatic environment. They are more varied and proceed at more rapid rates under warmer conditions. The development of meltwater, especially in copious amounts, is especially significant with respect to both densification and thermal relations. Meltwater develops at the surface and percolates down into the underlying permeable material where it refreezes as long as that material is at temperatures below 0° C. A certain amount of dispersed percolation must occur, but in addition a lot of the percolating water is channeled into essentially vertical, cylindrical "pipes" that extend downward 5 to 10 feet from the surface. Meltwater spreads out laterally from these "pipes" along pervious strata or on top of impervious layers in the snow or firn where it refreezes to form ice lenses and layers. This is one of the ways by which the original stratification is accentuated.

The cause of channelization into the "pipes" is not clear. It may involve irregularities on the snow surface or internal inhomogeneities within the snow. Once started a "pipe" seems to be a self-enforcing phenomenon which grows and maintains itself as long as the supply of meltwater continues. Eventually, perhaps because of a change in weather, the water supply is cut off. When this happens the percolated water quickly refreezes by loss of heat to the surrounding cold firn and snow. This forms a crude vertical column of ice within the snow with horizontally projecting ice layers and lenses (Fig. 6). Features of this type have been observed in the snow and firn of a number of glaciers, and the process has actually been witnessed in action near the edge of the Greenland Ice Sheet by Carl Benson.

The percolation and refreezing process goes on principally during spring and early summer when significant melting first occurs and when the underlying material still contains the winter's chill. An annual snow or firn layer may be exposed to several cycles of meltwater percolation and freezing before it becomes too deeply buried to be affected by seasonal temperature variations. The conversion of snow to solid ice proceeds much less rapidly in cold areas devoid of meltwater. Here grain deformation, vapor transfer, and possibly local pressure melting must play a relatively larger role.

The Entrapped Gas

Most glacier ice contains a considerable number of small bubbles. These are filled principally with air that was trapped in the snow of the accumulation area, but they may also include dissolved gases given up by water upon freezing. The bubbles have been isolated, to a greater or lesser degree, since the pores were sealed off in the process of converting snow to solid ice. The nature of the entrapped air may have been subsequently modified by partial solution of its constituents in meltwater, by the release of dissolved gases through freezing of water, by mixing with other air during progressive recrystallization of the ice, and perhaps by diffusion although this is a slow progress. In favorable instances the entrapped air could represent a sample of the atmosphere as it was hundreds and in some instances thousands of years ago. Preliminary studies of the gas by Scholander, Coachman and Nutt have yielded some tantalizing data, the meanings of which are not yet clear. The entrapped CO_2 can be used to determine the age of the ice by radio carbon (C^{14}) dating, although the problems of evaluating contamination by modern CO_2 are difficult. This looks like an interesting and promising line of investigation which should be watched carefully.

Summation

In time, accumulated snow gradually changes to firn and then to glacier ice. The density, grain size, compactness and hardness all increase, and the original layered structure can be accentuated. The porosity and permeability decrease. The initial snow was in effect an eolian sediment, and it is converted to a sedimentary rock by various diagenetic changes. Once the material is caught up in the flow of the glacier, it is rapidly converted to a metamorphic rock with structures, fabrics and other features characteristic thereof. The sedimentary features are not necessarily immediately or completely destroyed, but they do become obscure. The accumulation basin is the realm of sedimentary deposition and of the initial alteration converting the material to glacier ice. The sedimentary blanket may rest upon a basement of metamorphic ice, but this is not exposed above the firn edge of the glacier. The lower bare ice tongue is the realm of the metamorphic material, and more will be said about its interesting structures later.

THE FLOW OF GLACIERS

Differences in the Speed of Flow
as Measured Along a Line Across a Glacier

Glaciers differ from other bodies of landborne ice in their ability to flow. This distinguishing behavior has long fascinated scientists and laymen alike, even to the point of a humorous treatment by the redoubtable Mark Twain. Records of surface-velocity measurements on valley glaciers go back at least 200 years.

Early investigators in the Alps showed that straight lines of markers laid across a glacier were, in due time, deformed into parabolic curves (Fig. 7, A). Much later, repeated photographs of some rapidly flowing

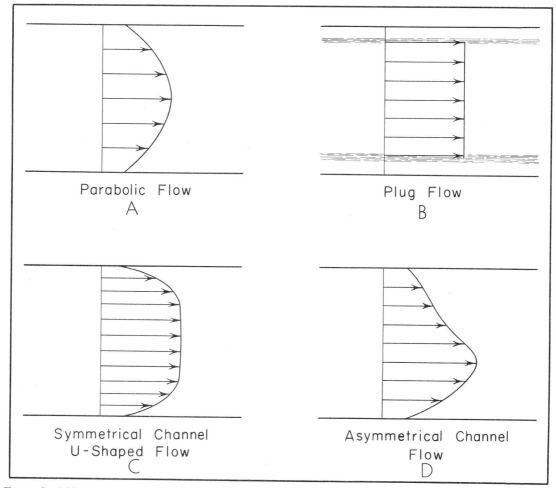

FIRURE 7. Different types of surface-velocity distribution along transverse profiles across valley glaciers.

glaciers in the Himalayas showed that the entire central parts of these glaciers move with a uniform velocity past marginal zones of nearly stationary ice. In these glaciers the change from essentially no movement to maximum movement occurs within narrow zones near the margins of the glacier (Fig. 7, B). This mode of movement has been called plug flow, because the central part moves as a plug past essentially stationary borders.

Measurements of surface velocity using more closely spaced markers suggest that the flow curve across many valley glaciers is intermediate between the parabolic and plug-flow types. As shown by this curve, which for want of a better term we shall call U-shaped, the central part of the glacier moves at a nearly uniform velocity, and the transition to slower movement near the valley walls occurs rapidly in narrow marginal zones (Fig. 7, C). Velocity profiles across the Saskatchewan, the Blue and other glaciers (Figs 8 and 9) suggest that this sort of transverse velocity curve is probably the most common, although for some reason we tend to overlook this fact.

In evaluating the meaning of the shape of a transverse velocity curve, one must remember that the surface velocity is strongly influenced by the thickness of the glacier and the steepness of its slope. Variations in either or both factors affect the shape and symmetry of the velocity curve. Since the surface velocity is greatest where the ice is thickest, other influences being equal, one would expect that a channel with a U-shaped cross section would produce a U-shaped velocity curve. It does, but a parabolic channel can also yield a U-shaped velocity curve. This happens because of the manner in which ice yields to stress.

To understand this matter it is helpful to make a plot showing the

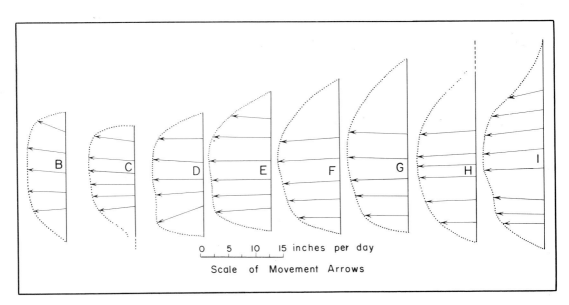

FIGURE 8. Horizontal component of surface velocity along a series of transverse profiles from firn edge (I) nearly to terminus (B) of Blue Glacier as measured in 1957-58. Note decrease of velocity near terminus and flow toward margins in terminal region (B).

difference in rates at which various substances yield to different degrees of stress. This is known as a stress and rate-of-strain diagram. On such a diagram (Fig. 10), we have plotted the relationships for three types of material, A, B and C. A is a so-called Newtonian fluid, such as water, in which the rate of yielding (strain) increases in a steady, regular manner as the stress (force per unit area) is increased. This gives a straight line of constant slope on the diagram. B is a perfectly plastic substance that doesn't yield at all until a certain threshold value of stress is exceeded, after which it theoretically yields at an infinite rate. It gives a straight horizontal line on our plot. C is ice which yields at a changing rate as the stress increases, and this produces a curved line on our plot. This behavior is sort of half way between that of the plastic and viscous materials, and for this reason some people refer to ice as a pseudo-plastic or quasi-viscous substance. If ice behaved as a Newtonian viscous fluid, the transverse surface velocity curve would reflect rather faithfully

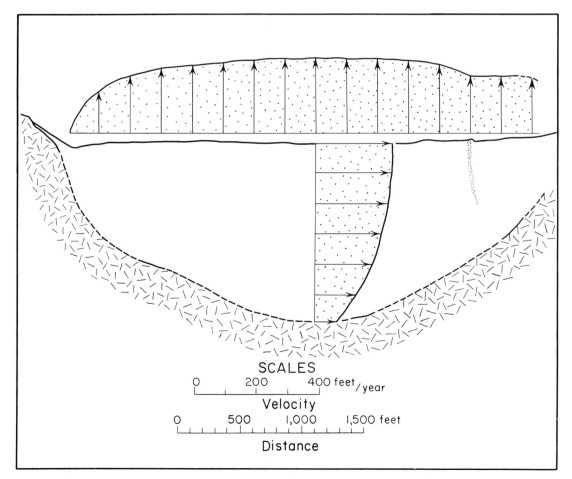

FIGURE 9. Measured transverse surface velocity profile (horizontal component) on Saskatchewan Glacier and calculated vertical velocity profile. To get proper picture, reader should imagine velocity profiles folded back so they are perpendicular to plane of the page. (After M. F. Meier).

the cross-section shape of the glacier's channel. The U-shaped velocity curve of a glacier flowing in a parabolic channel is thus a reflection of the fact that the yielding curve of ice under the increasing stress caused by increasing thickness has the shape of a half-U (Fig. 10, C).

Magnitude and Variations of Flow Velocity

Everyone seems to be interested in the speed of glacier movement. Unless otherwise specified, the figures cited below refer to the maximum surface velocity near the center. Many valley glaciers flow with a speed of 1 to 2 feet per day. In steep reaches, the movement can be 10 or even 20 feet per day, and over icefalls it may be still greater. Velocities up to 125 feet per day have been measured on the huge outlet glaciers of the Greenland Ice Sheet. Sudden short-lived advances of valley glaciers have occurred in the Himalayas, the Andes, and Alaska for which velocities of 100 to 370 feet per day have been estimated. During a brief advance in 1937, the Black Rapids Glacier in Alaska may have attained a velocity of 250 feet per day. These spectacular speeds are truly exceptional, and most of the glaciers that we see move only a few feet per day at most.

Seasonal variations in the movement of valley glaciers have been recorded. It is commonly stated that movement in the accumulation area is greater during winter because of the increased load of snow. Conversely, the flow is supposedly greatest in the ablation area during

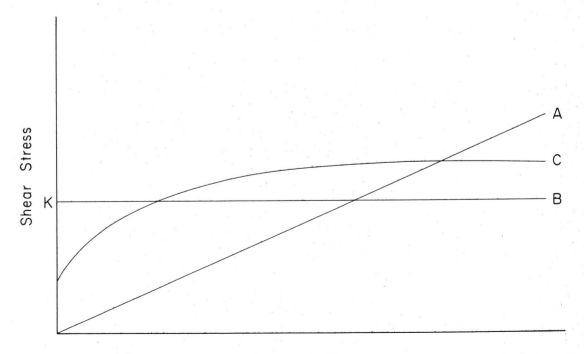

Rate of Strain

FIGURE 10. The relationship of rate of strain to stress for a Newtonian viscous material (A), a perfectly plastic substance (B), and ice (C), as determined by laboratory experiments.

summer because of warmer temperatures and a copious supply of melt-water. These statements may well represent oversimplifications, and the causes are not necessarily those specified. Seasonal variations in glacier movement need much more study.

Some measurements have been made suggesting that glaciers experience variations in velocity within periods of a few hours or days. Although such movements are often erratic; in some instances a regular diurnal cycle is said to exist, and variations in flow appear to be related to changes in weather conditions. Some of the earlier measurements made may not have been rigorously controlled, and others are possibly not accurate enough to justify the conclusions reached. However, it is certain that variations of small magnitude do occur, but apparent relationships to variations in temperature or other meteorological elements have not yet been satisfactorily explained in terms of cause and effect. It seems that major storms, particularly those with heavy rain, can have a marked temporary effect on velocity, but the reasons for this are not yet known. Short-time variations of glacier flow constitute an interesting facet of glaciological research worthy of more study than it has yet received.

Basal Slip and Internal Flow

The surface movement is produced by slippage of the ice over its floor and by internal flow within the glacier (Fig. 11). Basal slip may account for most of the movement of thin, cold glaciers resting on steep slopes or for only 10 to 20 per cent of the movement of warm, thick glaciers lying on gentle slopes. Adequate testimony to the existence of basal slippage is given by the ice-scoured bedrock surfaces across which glaciers have moved (Plate 8, B).

Attempts to determine the proportionate contributions of internal flow and basal slip have been made by boring vertical holes into glaciers and measuring the subsequent deformation of pipes left in the holes. Investigations of this type have been undertaken on glaciers in the Alps, Alaska, Canada and the United States. Figure 12 presents vertical velocity profiles, or flow curves, obtained from holes in the Malaspina and Blue glaciers. These curves show that the surface is carried along by movement of the underlying ice and that the differential rate of flow increases with depth.

About 20 years ago much attention was given an hypothesis suggesting that ice at depth in a sheet resting on a flat surface would be squeezed out or extruded by the weight of the overlying material, more or less like paste from a tube. Initially, this concept was favorably regarded in some quarters, but physicists have since shown on theoretical grounds that extrusion flow is not only unlikely but indeed downright impossible in most glaciers. Data from boreholes on the Jungfraujoch in Switzerland and the Malaspina Glacier indicate that extrusion flow does not occur in these two bodies, although it should if the concept were valid.

The Actual Direction of Flow

For some reason most of us are inclined to think of the flow of a glacier as parallel to its surface. In most parts of the glacier the true direction of movement is *not* parallel to the surface, and most of the

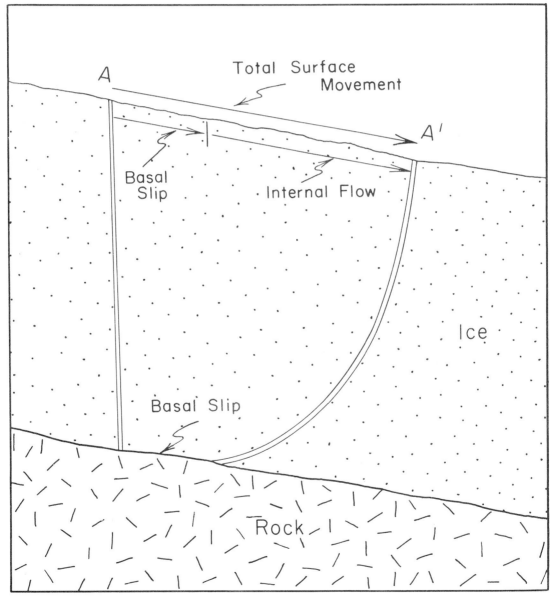

FIGURE 11. Sketch illustrating that surface movement on a glacier is produced partly by slip over the floor at its base and partly by internal deformation.

values reported for surface velocities represent only that part of the motion that is parallel to the surface or parallel to the horizontal plane of a map.

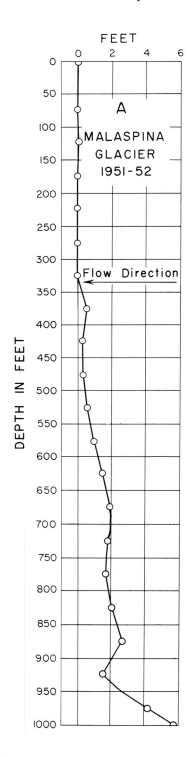

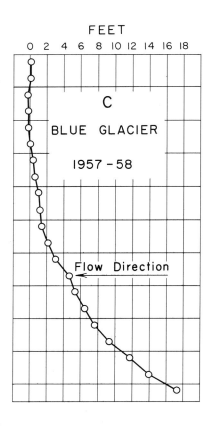

FIGURE 12. Deformation by glacier flow of pipes in deep bore-holes. A—Malaspina Glacier 1000-foot hole, 1951-52; B—Upper 300 feet of the Malaspina hole, 1951-54; C—Blue Glacier, 1957-58. All show maximum movement at the surface but greater differential movement with depth. Curve B demonstrates that measurable deformation occurs within ice close to the surface in a period of 3 years. If extrusion flow were a valid concept, its effects would show in curve A, which they do not. Note horizontal scale is exaggerated with respect to vertical scale, and horizontal scale for curve C is one-half that of curves A and B.

Many years ago the American glaciologist Harry Fielding Reid, deduced that the actual directions of flow in a valley glacier should be obliquely downward in the accumulation area and obliquely upward in the wastage area, as illustrated in Figure 1. He arrived at this conclusion partly through the realization that the snow layer added each year in the accumulation area is wedge-shaped, thickest at the glacier head and thinning to an edge at the snowline. A somewhat similar wedge, thickest near the terminus, is removed each year in the wastage area. Clearly, a glacier could maintain its surface profile most easily in the face of these wedge-shaped changes by movements oblique to rather than parallel to the surface as illustrated (Fig. 1). The component of downward movement, *with respect to the surface*, should increase toward the head of the glacier, and the component of upward movement should increase toward the terminus. Flow in the vicinity of the annual snowline should be essentially parallel to the surface.

Measurements of the absolute directions of movement made in the ablation areas of the Saskatchewan and Blue glaciers show that it is generally slightly upward *with respect to the surface* but *not* with respect to the horizontal (Fig. 13). With exceptions, the upward angle increases slightly toward the terminus. Nowhere is the angle large, and diagrams drawn by Reid and others after him, including myself, probably err in showing the flow lines as rising too steeply. They may also be incorrect in indicating movement upward from the horizontal. Unfortunately, corresponding data on actual directions of movement have not yet been obtained from the accumulation areas of these glaciers.

As viewed in a horizontal rather than a vertical plane the direction of flow is also not always directly downglacier. The direction of flow is controlled primarily by the direction of slope of the ice surface. Most valley glaciers have a slightly convex transverse profile in the wastage area caused by greater melting along the margins. Because of this, some flow of ice obliquely toward the margins should be expected, and has been recorded on the Saskatchewan and Blue glaciers (Fig. 8 and 14). This direction of flow enables glaciers to replace ice destroyed by marginal melting and helps maintain the transverse profile. One should

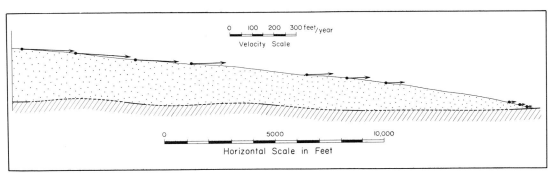

FIGURE 13. True direction and amount of flow as recorded along a central flowline on the Saskatchewan Glacier. Note that flow directions are slightly upward with respect to the glacier surface and that movement is much slower near the terminus. (After M. F. Meier).

expect to find just the reverse relationship above the annual snowline in places of exceptionally heavy marginal accumulation, and inward flow from the margins has been recorded in such situations.

Longitudinal Variations in Flow

The largest volume of ice being handled by a glacier is at the annual snowline. This must be so, for the total amount of ice increases progressively to the snowline because of accumulation and progressively decreases below it through wastage. In a glacier of uniform cross section and uniform longitudinal slope, the surface velocity must also have its greatest value at the annual snowline. In such a glacier the average velocity should increase from the head of the glacier to the snowline and decrease from there to the terminus. Few glaciers are of uniform cross section and slope, but allowing for irregularities in both factors, a decrease in surface velocity downglacier from the snowline is shown by both the Saskatchewan and Blue glaciers (Figs. 8 and 14). Corresponding data above the snowline are lacking.

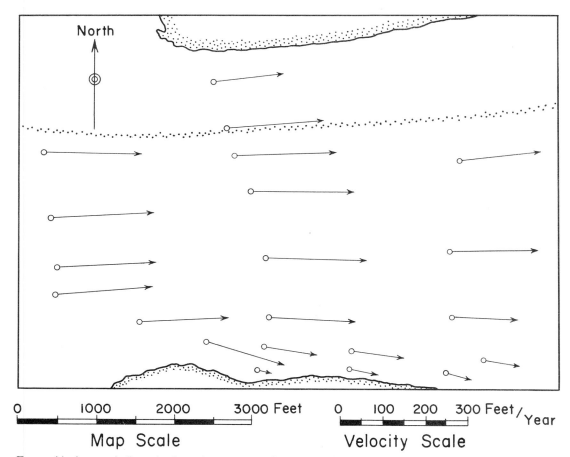

FIGURE 14. Arrows indicate horizontal component of annual surface movement on Saskatchewan Glacier about 2 miles below firn edge. Note flow obliquely toward south margin, presumably because of excessive ablation and local widening of the valley.

Actually, much larger and more abrupt changes in velocity are caused by variations in channel characteristics, particularly slope. What happens when a glacier slows down over a gentle reach in its course? The ice farther upglacier doesn't know anything about this, except possibly for a local "back water" effect, and it keeps moving along at its usual pace pouring material into the gentler reach. The result is that ice tends to pile up in the gentle reach, and the glacier becomes thicker until it can handle the discharge at the slower velocity. Rivers of water do the same thing, slow flowing parts are deep. This behavior in glaciers has been termed "compressive flow" by John Nye of Bristol, England, who has demonstrated on a mathematical and physical basis, how and why it occurs. One should not be misled by the term "compressive." Ice in glaciers is to all intent and purpose essentially an incompressible solid. Except for elimination of air bubbles the ice remains unchanged in density, the only compression that occurs is a shortening of a unit of ice which is balanced by its increase in thickness.

Nye has also demonstrated that steep reaches with accelerating velocity produce an extension of the glacier, with a reduction in thickness and the formation of crevasses. This he designates "extending flow." It occurs, for example, as a glacier descends an icefall, and the ice becomes several times thinner than it was above. It is also badly crevassed. In the "plunge pool," at the base of the icefall, extreme compressive flow occurs, and the ice builds up to a thickness several times that in the icefall, the crevasses are forced shut, and the broken ice debris that has fallen into them is severely squeezed.

Practically all glaciers undergo at least a modest degree of extending and compressive flow because of differential accumulation and wastage. However, the areas of strong compression and extension are related to abrupt changes in longitudinal gradient. The concept of these types of flow developed by Nye is one of the most useful ideas to have appeared in glaciology in decades. It helps immeasurably in understanding glacier behavior and in interpreting the structures seen within them.

Surges in Glaciers

For many years it has been known that bulges of increased thickness descend through valley glaciers at a velocity several times the normal speed of flow. We now realize that many of the recorded erratic and sudden advances of glacier snouts are the result of the arrival of such bulges at the glacier terminus. The movement of a bulge through the Nisqually Glacier on Mount Rainier in Washington, has been under observation now for nearly 15 years. The events attending its arrival at the terminus, if it gets that far, are awaited with interest.

A theoretical analysis of the behavior of waves in glaciers suggests that the bulges, better termed surges, should move with velocities about 3 to 8 times greater than the normal speed of flow. Surge velocities about 4 times normal have actually been observed. It appears that a general disturbance in the headwaters can generate a series of surges. Those of high velocity overtake and enforce slow-moving surges so that the phenomenon which ultimately arrives at the terminus may have some of the characteristics of a shock wave. Perhaps, this is one reason why the behavior of the glacier snout is so unusual. Surges need not be limited to valley glaciers. Our experiences suggest that one moved through the borehole site on the Malaspina Glacier, a piedmont ice sheet, between the summers of 1953 and 1954.

The general tendency is to attribute surges to episodes of increased accumulation in the headwaters. This possibility is supported by the behavior of glaciers in the Yakutat Bay area of Alaska following the powerful Yakutat Bay earthquakes in 1899. Many of these glaciers experienced sudden short-lived advances a few years after the earthquakes. Various lines of reasoning led to the conclusion that this behavior was best explained by the movement of surges through these glaciers, and it was postulated that these surges were generated by the large amounts of snow avalanched onto the headwaters of the glaciers by the earthquakes. Many other spectacular, short-lived advances, seemingly unrelated to earthquakes or even to known periods of exceptional accumulation, have been reported from Alaska, the Alps, the Andes and the Himalayas.

In this regard the recent behavior of Muldrow Glacier draining off the east slopes of Mt. McKinley in Alaska is particularly informative. The lower reach of this glacier has been relatively inactive, even locally stagnant, for a long time. Suddenly during the winter of 1956-57 it showed a spectacular renewal of activity, and the terminus advanced rapidly. Morainal features on the upper part of the ice tongue also moved downward rapidly. The important thing is that there is no reason to attribute this behavior to a sudden increase in accumulation of either earthquake or meteorological origin. Following the advance, it was noted that the ice level in the upper reaches of several of the important tributaries of the Muldrow system had dropped by several tens of feet. The volume of ice supplied by this drop is about right to account for the advance and expansion of the lower part of the glacier. It looks as though the Muldrow Glacier had slowly been accumulating material for many years, up to a certain threshold amount. At this point a sudden evacuation from the accumulation area began to occur which gave rise to a surge or series of surges that moved rapidly downglacier and ultimately produced the great changes recorded in the lower reaches. This is not a new concept by any means, but the recent Muldrow Glacier behavior is one of the best documented cases on record.

The behavior of surges in glaciers is currently a topic of high interest in glaciology. We need more observation of this phenomenon in the field to support the excellent theoretical treatments made by Weertman, Nye and others.

The Mechanics of Movement

Ice is clearly a solid substance, but it is equally clear that large bodies of ice will flow with great facility, given time. Just how does ice flow, what are the detailed mechanics of the process, and do several different mechanisms contribute to the total effect? Or is it likely that different mechanisms play the dominant role under different conditions? Glaciologists have struggled with these problems for a long time, so let us review briefly their thoughts on these matters.

Adjustments between grains have long been highly regarded as a possible means of glacier flow. This involves the movement of individual grains (crystals) past one another as might occur in a bean bag or a sack of lead shot (Fig. 15, B). Intergranular adjustments could occur freely and easily in loose snow or firn, and studies of changes in crystallographic orientation of firn grains indicate that such adjustments are common in early stages of the compaction process. However, are they equally common in solid glacier ice made up of crystals firmly grown together? The possibility of intergranular adjustments in such

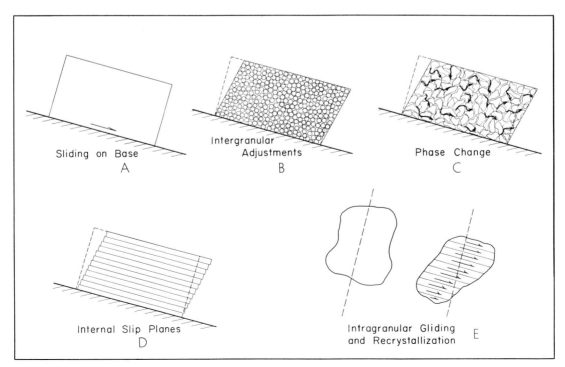

FIGURE 15. Sketches illustrating various possible mechanisms of glacier movement.

material cannot be hastily dismissed in view of the extended time available and the assistance afforded by local pressure melting and vapor transfer. However, some glacier ice consists of crystals so intimately and complexly intergrown that no flow or deformation is possible even though the crystals are completely loose. They are held together in the manner of a three-dimensional jig-saw puzzle. Furthermore, the strong preferred crystallographic orientation found in glacier ice suggests that intergranular shifting is minimal. For these reasons, intergranular adjustments are no longer so highly regarded as a major mechanism of solid flow in glaciers. They may be the principal means by which snow deforms, and they could contribute in limited degree to glacier flow under proper conditions.

A once-favored mechanism of flow depends upon local and temporary changes of ice to the liquid or vapor phases (Fig. 15, C). The thought is that local stresses, crystal configuration or energy distribution cause some of the ice to melt or vaporize. This vapor or liquid is then supposed to move a short distance before reverting to the solid state, thus effecting a transport of material. Changes of phase could promote intergranular adjustments, and the homogenization of oxygen isotopes that occurs within glaciers is one reason for thinking that such changes may occur. However, the movement of the liquid would probably be controlled by capillarity, and there is no obvious reason why either it or the vapor should move predominantly in a downglacier direction. Furthermore, laboratory tests show that ice can be made to flow at temperatures well below those at which pressure melting would occur. The phase-change mechanism may function, but it is probably not of major importance in most situations.

A solid body can be deformed by a series of small displacements along a multitude of closely spaced parallel planes (Fig. 15, D). Slippage of the individual playing cards within a deck affords a good analogy. Structures observed in glaciers suggest that such slip displacements occur locally, and on a limited scale, but the phenomenon does not appear pervasive enough or of sufficient magnitude to account for most glacier movement.

This brings us to a final possibility which currently is highly regarded. It holds that ice flows principally because of adjustments that occur within the individual ice crystals (Fig. 15E). This is known as *intragranular* yielding as compared to *intergranular* adjustments; the two should not be confused. It has long been known that an ice crystal yields easily to shear stress by gliding along the basal crystallographic plane. This is a process which does not destroy the solidity or coherence of the material and does not alter or disrupt the internal atomic arrangement of the crystal. Its occurrence has been demonstrated repeatedly by laboratory experiments. The fact that crystals in a glacier display a strongly preferred orientation is taken as evidence in support of intracrystalline yielding as a principal mechanism of glacier flow. Continued internal gliding of the crystals would eventually distort them into grossly elongated shapes unlike anything usually seen in glaciers. Therefore, it is postulated that a progressive recrystallization accompanies the intracrystalline gliding, and that this maintains the crystals in their roughly equidimensional form. Recrystallization of this type has been demonstrated in the laboratory, and it is one of the mechanisms by which crystals arrange themselves into the proper orientation for yielding by intracrystalline gliding. This need not be the only mechanism of solid flow in glacier ice, but it is currently regarded as one of major significance.

STRUCTURES IN GLACIERS

General Statement

Although we don't usually think of it as such, snow is a sediment that settles out of the atmosphere onto the earth's surface. A snowbank is therefore actually an eolian sedimentary deposit in geological parlance. Since snowbanks are the forerunners of glaciers, glaciers are initially sedimentary bodies, and they have various structures, especially stratification, reflecting that mode of origin. Once the glacier starts to move, it enters the metamorphic realm and within a short time the sedimentary structures are greatly modified, obscured, and eventually they may be destroyed. Stratification inherited from the sedimentary accumulation basin is usually a prominent feature in the ice tongue only of small glaciers. Most structures seen in the ice tongue are the product of deformation and metamorphism. They make interesting subjects of study for geologists, because glacier ice is one of the few solid earth materials that undegoes deformation on the earth's surface under a temperature at or close to its melting point. One can observe this deformation at close hand, relate it to the deforming stresses and compare the structures created to those formed by similar deformation in rocks deep within the earth's crust where direct observation is not possible.

Crevasses

Crevasses are elongate open cracks that form in the surficial part of a glacier where stretching caused by differences in rates of flow exceeds the breaking strength. The cracks that form within a coating of a brittle substance on a rubber sheet when the sheet is stretched would be somewhat analagous. Crevasses are one of the earliest structural features appearing in a glacier, and they develop in all its parts from head to terminus. When first formed they are perpendicular to the direction of greatest elongation or stretching, and they may curve if the direction of stretching changes along the lateral extent of the crevasse. They can be rotated, deformed and even squeezed shut by subsequent flow. The nature, orientation, and arrangement of crevasses thus provide useful information on the flow behavior of an ice stream.

Few crevasses in valley glaciers are more than 100 to 150 feet deep, partly because greater plastic flow at depth keeps them closed or because the deeper ice is less brittle and does not fracture readily. Most crevasses in small valley glaciers are only a few feet wide at the top, but in especially steep reaches they may be tens of feet wide.

Crevasses form abundantly in areas where a marked steepening of slope causes the flow velocity to increase rapidly. They also develop in zones where the transverse surface velocity changes rapidly, as along the lateral margins of an ice stream. Crevasses, especially in icefalls, tend to become partly or wholly filled with snow, firn and ice breccia derived from avalanches and the fall of ice blocks from the crevasse walls. Icefall crevasses are usually squeezed shut within the zone of strong compression at the base of the fall. Consequently, the breccias within them are compressed and greatly modified giving rise to some of the principal structural features seen in the ice tongue.

The crevasses of valley glaciers can be described in terms of their orientation with respect to the long dimension of the body as transverse, longitudinal, or oblique. They can also be identified by location, for example as marginal, central or terminal (Plate 9, A). Transverse crevasses extending more or less completely across a glacier are usually related to a steepening of the glacier's slope. Their initial shape and orientation reflect the geometry of the steeper slope in relation to the direction of flow. Initially, such crevasses are usually concave down-glacier (Plate 9, B), but they can be subsequently deformed into straight lines or even into convex arcs by the more rapid movement of the central ice (Fig. 16, B).

Marginal crevasses (Plate 9, A) are formed by stretching related to the rapid change in velocity that occurs between ice streams or along the margins of a glacier. They are initially directed about 45° up-glacier (Fig. 16, A) but are soon rotated and deformed by the high degree of differential flow occurring within these zones (Plate 12, A). By the time they have been rotated roughly 30°, a new set of crevasses forms to relieve the newly accumulated elastic stretching. Intersecting sets of crevasses are thus common in marginal zones of valley glaciers. An extremely narrow zone of closely spaced crevasses along the edges of a valley glacier suggests that the movement is more of the plug-flow type then parabolic (Fig. 7). Longitudinal crevasses develop in places where the glacier is spreading out or extending itself laterally. This happens most commonly near the terminus, especially on receding glaciers where lateral confinement is likely to be minimal. Short longitudinal crevasses with some suggestion of a radial or fan-like arrangement are not uncommon near the terminus of a glacier (Fig. 16, D). Radial crevasses are also characteristic of lobate or bulbous ice masses and of piedmont ice sheets like Malaspina Glacier. In those reaches of a valley glacier undergoing a modest degree of compressive flow, longitudinal crevasses may form in the central part of the ice stream. These

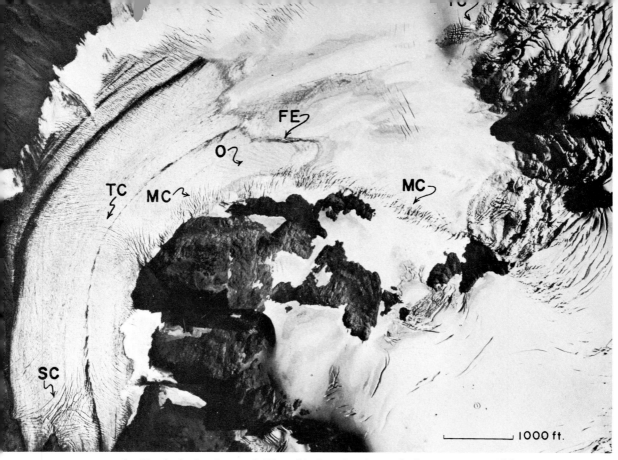

1000 ft.

A—Vertical air photo of Blue Glacier showing splaying crevasses (SC) near terminus, transverse crevasses (TC) in middle reach, marginal crevasses (MC), and ticktacktoe crevasse pattern (TTC). Also shown are the firn edge (FE), faint ogives (O), and the icefall at the right margin of the photo. September 11, 1957.

Plate 9

B—Transverse crevasses in lower Blue Glacier, Olympic Mountains, Washington, as viewed from west valley wall in August, 1958. Glacier flows to left and initial concavity of crevasse traces is partly straightened out downvalley by differential flow.

A—Exposure on the wall of a crevasse in Saskatchewan Glacier, Canada, showing gently inclined, slightly folded sedimentary layering cut by near-vertical foliation which is essentially parallel to the ice axe.

Plate 10

B—Near-vertical well-developed foliation along the west margin of the Blue Glacier involving an interlayering of coarse-bubbly, coarse-clear and fine ice.

usually curve around into an oblique orientation at the margins (Fig. 16, C). Mark Meier has happily termed them splaying crevasses. They develop with this orientation because the axis of greatest extension is at right angles to the longitudinal compression in the center of the glacier and rotates gradually to an angle of 45° near the margins. Splaying crevasses are probably more common in valley glaciers than most of us realize, and Nye has given a good explanation of their origin in terms of the pattern of deforming forces associated with compressive flow.

Many other types of crevasses are known. Some are local and related to particular stress conditions caused by aberrant geometrical relationships. A good example would be the ticktacktoe crevasse pattern of the Blue Glacier (Plate 9, A), which is probably produced by a rock knob on the valley floor.

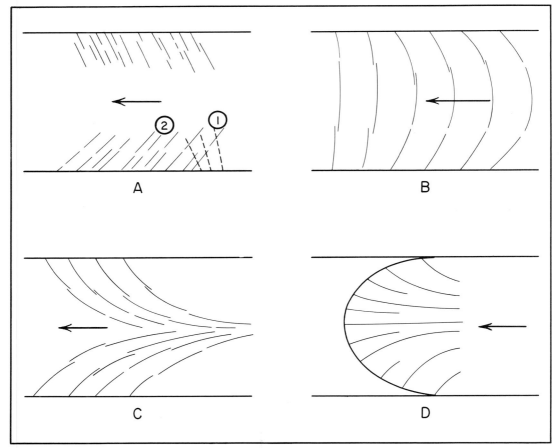

FIGURE 16. Principal types of crevasses in valley glaciers. A—Marginal, 1) old rotated crevasses, 2) newly formed crevasses; B—Transverse; C—Splaying; D—Radial splaying. Arrow indicates flow direction.

Medial Moraines and Other Longitudinal Septa

The dark streaks of rocky debris that we see on the surfaces of many valley glaciers, such as the Barnard (Plate 4, B) and the Kaskawulsh (Plate 5, A), show that these glaciers are made up of a number of ice streams. These streams represent individual glaciers from tributary valleys that have flowed together and are now separated only by thin partitions (septa) of dirty ice containing rock material picked up from the walls of the tributary valleys. Melting of this dirty ice produces a surficial accumulation of detritus which constitutes the feature known as a medial moraine. It is well to remember that this accumulation is simply the surface expression of a structure that extends deeply into the glacier, usually to its floor except in the instance of inset ice streams (Fig. 2, p. 13).

A less apparent but structurally more significant type of longitudinal septum has recently been recognized on the Blue Glacier (Fig. 17), and a somewhat similar feature has been earlier described from the Pasterze Glacier in Austria. The longitudinal septum on the Blue is a zone of highly foliated, structurally complex material containing an exceptionally large amount of fine ice. It is about 250 feet wide at the firn edge and narrows to 10 or 20 feet near the terminus. In the field we refer to the Blue Glacier spetum as the *Gesundheitstrasse*, and that designation will be used here from force of habit. This is an important feature as it divides the ice tongue into two structurally distinct units. It appears to be formed near the base of the icefall by the reunion of two ice currents split apart by a large rock bastion (Fig. 18). One current flows into a depression below the rock bastion almost at right angles to the other. The ice of the first current undergoes severe compression and is also sheared out by the difference in velocity of the two currents. These actions produce an exceptionally strong foliation. A large amount of snow is also incorporated into the *Gesundheitstrasse* by the filling of abnormally abundant crevasses and by infolding in the depression below the rock bastion. The fact that the width and strength of the *Gesundheitstrasse* decrease downglacier from the firn edge suggests that it is strongest near the surface and becomes weaker with depth. We suspect that additional *Gesundheitstrasse*-type features will be discovered in other glaciers as their structure is more thoroughly studied.

Foliation

The most pervasive structure of ice tongues is a banding or layering termed foliation (Plate 10, B). It has been seen by nearly all glacier travelers and corresponds to the layering observed in metamorphic rocks. It is regarded as a purely secondary structure produced by deformation associated with flow. Foliation is usually expressed by differences in the size and arrangement of ice crystals. Three types of ice are commonly involved in Blue Glacier foliation; specifically, coarse-bubbly, coarse-clear, and fine ice. The strongest foliation is that involving an

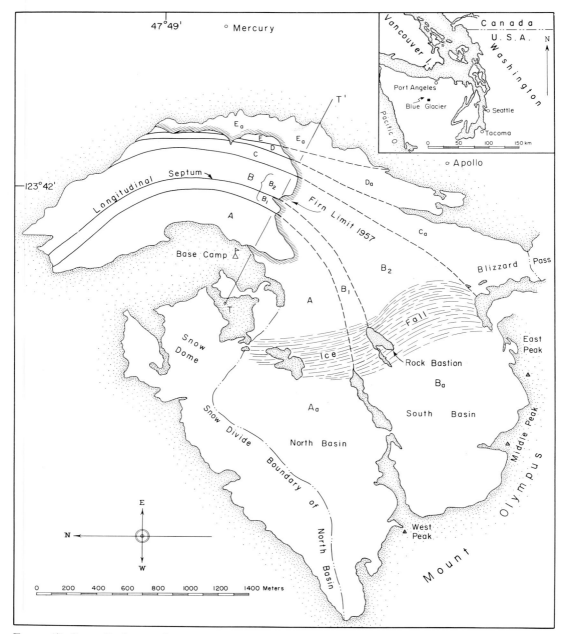

FIGURE 17. Generalized map of the Blue Glacier showing how it is made up of 5 separate ice streams (A to E) each draining from its own area of accumulation (A_a to E_a). Ice stream B is split into two parts (B_1 and B_2) by a rock bastion, and these parts are then separated by the Longitudinal Septum or *Gesundheitstrasse*.

interlayering of these types of ice (Plate 11, A). Foliation may also
be produced by differences in air-bubble distribution within coarse-

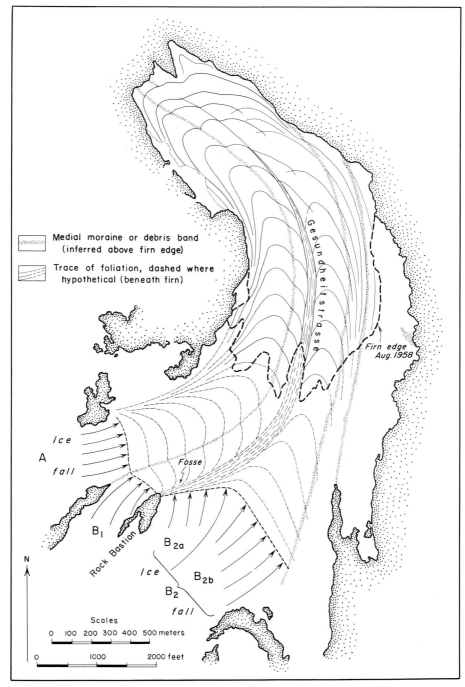

FIGURE 18. Map showing in simplified manner principal structures of lower Blue Glacier ice
tongue and inferred directions of flow (arrows) within and at base of icefall.

A—Close-up view of foliation in a block of ice about 12 inches across. Dark bands are clear ice, white bands in middle are fine ice, less whitish bands at outer edges are composed of coarse-bubbly ice.

Plate 11

B—Air view of valley glacier in Yakutat Range east of Yakutat, Alaska. Note the double arcuate pattern of foliation visible in the two central ice streams. Late August, 1951.

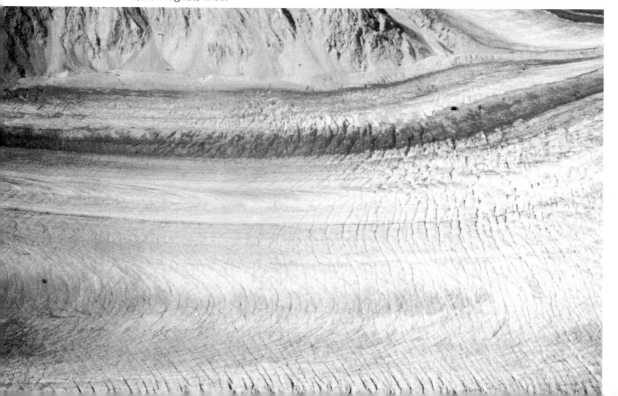

bubbly ice, and some fine ice displays a foliation created by a preferred orientation of elongated grains.

The strength and degree of development of foliation vary widely within a single glacier and from one glacier to another. It is often brought into relief on the surface by differential melting, and it can be beautifully exposed on the walls of crevasses (Plate 10, B). Foliation can be so weak near the center of an ice stream that it may be difficult to see at all.

One of the notable things about foliation is the geometrical patterns in which it occurs. In most glaciers foliation is well-developed in zones close to the margins where it is parallel to the valley walls (Plate 10, B) except as distorted by small folds (Plate 13, A) and displacements along fractures. Near the terminus, the foliation usually swings into an arc that crosses the glacier joining the two marginal zones of longitudinal foliation. The foliation planes at the apex of this arc are inclined upglacier between 20° and 40° from the horizontal. Along the margins they are inclined more steeply, commonly 60° to 80°, inward toward the center.

In glaciers with icefalls, a transverse foliation pattern may appear throughout the ice tongue below the icefall, not just at the terminus. If the glacier is made up of more than one ice stream, each may display its own foliation pattern (Plate 11, B). The Blue Glacier provides a good example of this sort of arrangement as it has an eastern and a western set of nested foliation arcs, convex downglacier, separated by the *Gesundheitstrasse* (Plate 12, A; Fig. 19). Near the firn edge the inclination of these foliation planes is steep, 80° to 85° inward toward the concave side of the arc, even at the apexes. Farther downvalley the upglacier inclination at the apex of the arcs gets progressively gentler, decreasing to 20° or less near the terminus. From surface observations, this structure is assumed to have the three-dimensional form of a series of nested spoons. Calculations, based on formulas involving the flow law of ice and on data from boreholes providing information on the flow curve at depth (Fig. 12), show that the downglacier decrease in inclination can be due to the differential flow occurring within the glacier. The greater movement of ice near the surface than at depth is of about the right amount to account for the differences in inclinations observed.

Foliation is probably created by an intense compression or shearing that squeezes or stretches everything out into thin layers. The exact process is not yet clearly understood, but it may involve several mechanisms including recrystallization, redistribution of air bubbles, and the extreme flattening and drawing out of pre-existing inhomogeneities within the ice. Where does this occur? Since foliation planes of the western arc continue across the west medial moraine (Fig. 19), the

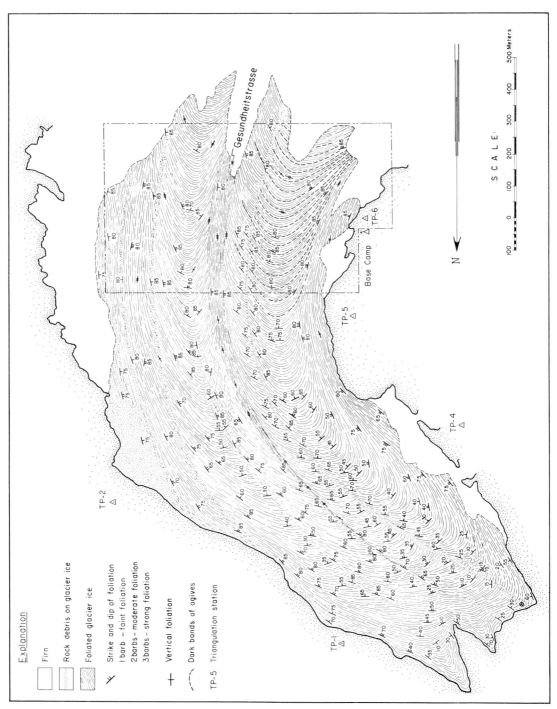

FIGURE 19. Structures exposed on surface of Blue Glacier below the firn edge as mapped in summer of 1959.

A—Middle reach of lower Blue Glacier as viewed from west wall showing double nested arc pattern in foliation, separated by the *Gesundheitstrasse*. Note rotated marginal crevasses at bottom of photo, some filled with snow and firn. 15 August, 1958.

Plate 12

B—Large crystals of glacier ice from stagnant margin of Malaspina Glacier.

arc pattern must be created somewhere below the junction of the ice streams separated by this moraine. This junction occurs well up in the icefall (Fig. 17). These relationships lead to the tentative conclusion that the transverse foliation of the Blue Glacier forms primarily within the zone of intense compression at the foot of the icefall, the so-called "structural mill." Inhomogeneities such as cracks, crevasses, insets of snow and firn-ice breccia and related features formed in the icefall are here severely squeezed and brought into a near-vertical transverse orientation. The foliation, is then deformed into an arc-like pattern within a short distance below the icefall by differential flow within the ice stream. The longitudinal foliation on the limbs of the arcs can be the product of shearing along the margins of the ice streams where the difference in flow velocities is relatively great.

The double-arc pattern of Blue Glacier is simplest and strongest where it first appears from beneath the blanket of firn (Plate 12, A). Downglacier it becomes generally weaker and is complicated by discordances in trend and by the local appearance of intersecting sets of foliation planes. Marked discordances can be seen in the western arc along the west medial moraine in the lower reach of the glacier and along the east side of the *Gesundheitstrasse* (Fig. 19). Intersecting sets of foliation planes appear within the western limb of the eastern arc in the middle reach of the glacier (Fig. 19). They show that not all of the foliation is formed at the same time. The double-arc pattern eventually gives way to an irregular single glacier-wide arc near the terminus.

It is well to remember that the surface of an ice tongue represents a highly oblique slice through the entire thickness of a glacier from its surface at the firn edge to its bottom at the terminus. Thus, structures seen on the surface in the lower reaches of a glacier presumably exist at depth somewhere farther upglacier. Consequently, the changes in the Blue Glacier foliation pattern appearing between the firn edge and the terminus reflect events and conditions existing farther upglacier. The transverse foliation pattern formed at the base of the icefall undergoes deformation and modification as it is carried downglacier (Fig. 18). In deep ice a new pattern may evolve gradually replacing the old one, and many of the irregularities seen in the lower part of the Blue Glacier may reflect irregularities on the glacier floor below the base of the icefall.

Ice-Crystal Relationships

Glaciers are made up of the crystals of a single mineral, ice. A glacier of any size contains literally millions of ice crystals, and it is worth looking into some of their relationships with each other and with the various features of the body they compose.

Most geological bodies that have been deformed reveal this in various ways, one of which is the preferred orientation displayed by the mineral crystals composing the body. Glacier ice has been deformed by flow; do its crystals show preferred orientation? The answer is emphatically yes.

George Rigsby has found from study of "cold" ice in Greenland that a large percentage of crystals are oriented so they can most easily yield to stress by internal crystallographic gliding just as one would expect. Much of the surface ice of warm glaciers has patterns of orientation in its crystals that are nearly as strong but considerably more complex. A common and striking pattern is one consisting of 4 centers of concentration arranged at the corners of a diamond-shaped rhomb that has a definite orientation with respect to the foliation. These multiple-center patterns are not yet well understood, but Barclay Kamb has shown by his work on the Blue Glacier that they have a consistent relationship to structures seen in the glacier and to the forces that are inferred to have created these structures. Some aspects of the complex patterns may be the result of a recrystallization that often takes place following relaxation of the deforming forces. In other words, the crystals of a glacier tend to arrange themselves as "comfortably" as possible in response to certain deforming forces. When these forces are relaxed, the crystals partly rearrange themselves into some other pattern which is more "comfortable" under the new conditions.

In addition to a preferred orientation, the ice crystals in a glacier display other interesting phenomena that can be more easily observed by the average glacier traveler. One of the more obvious of these is size. The ice granules in old snow and firn are equidimensional crystals usually less than a tenth of an inch in diameter. By the time the ice has moved into the tongue, hundreds of these little grains have been welded together into single crystals as much as several inches across (Plate 12, B). In old, far-traveled and now inactive ice at the edge of Malaspina Glacier, crystals 8 to 10 inches in diameter are not uncommon, and some attain a length of several feet. In general crystal size in glaciers has been found to increase with age, distance traveled and higher temperature, and to decrease with higher velocity, and greater stress. These influences can of course be conflicting, and the results do not always seem consistent.

The boundaries between ice crystals appear as irregular shallow grooves on the smooth walls or ceilings of ice caverns or on overhanging ice faces shaded from direct radiation. Exposures of this type are found chiefly in the marginal and terminal parts of an ice tongue where the crystals tend to be large. With a little care it is possible to separate a single ice crystal from its neighbors in a partly thawed chunk of ice. Melting occurs readily along the crystal contacts because of the impurities, including soluble salts, concentrated there by exclusion from the ice as it crystallized. The surface of the separated crystals appear to be riven by a multitude of tiny melt grooves, rather worm-like in shape and arrangement. On the partly melted surface of such a crystal one may also see a series of larger shallow parallel grooves known as Forel stripes or lines. These are formed by melting along basal planes of the ice crystal and can be used to determine its approximate crystallographic orientation.

In many instances the air bubbles inside a crystal are concentrated into bubble-rich and bubble-poor layers. A little study will usually show that these layers are parallel to and actually part of the foliated structure of the glacier. A single ice crystal may extend across several foliation bands in coarse-bubbly ice.

The most satisfying experience of all is to be successful in producing the spectacular little Tyndall melt figures within an ice crystal. These were named for the famed British physicist, John Tyndall, who did much excellent work on glaciers about 100 years ago. To obtain the figures, select a clear crystal and place it in direct sunshine for a few minutes. Eventually, a series of very thin flat circular discs about $\frac{1}{4}$ inch in diameter will appear inside the ice. These are hard to see until rotated into a position where complete reflection occurs, then they suddenly appear as silvery discs. Considerable twisting and turning of the crystal may be necessary before the right orientation is found. The Tyndall figures may appear elliptical rather than circular depending upon the angle at which they are viewed. They lie parallel to the basal crystallographic plane and all have exactly the same orientation. With continued melting the figures grow larger, and the outer edge of the disc becomes regularly crenulated with a pattern reflecting a 6-fold symmetry. These crenulated figures have been called Tyndall flowers.

The Tyndall figure is the product of local melting inside the ice caused by transmitted radiation. It consists of water containing a small bubble of vapor. Dr. Ukichiro Nakaya of the Snow, Ice and Permafrost Research Establishment has made a thorough study of these features illustrated by striking photographs. The figures can be made to disappear by refreezing.

Folds

Folds in glaciers are similar to folds in most other substances. They are recognizable because they involve visible planar features, which in the case of glaciers are chiefly foliation planes and morainal septa. The Saskatchewan Glacier affords an exception in that it displays a large fold nearly one mile wide and several miles long that involves sedimentary layering inherited from the accumulation basin. The inclination of the beds in this fold is gentle, and it is the outcrop pattern on the glacier surface (Plate 2, B) rather than the three dimensional relations that attracts attention. This structure is something of a puzzle, for the inclination of the beds is just the reverse of what would normally be expected from flow relations within the glacier. Much smaller folds involving either stratification or foliation are locally abundant along the margins of the Saskatchewan Glacier (Plate 13, A).

The lower reaches of some valley glaciers display large-scale folding of medial moraines. In some instances these are the product of spasmodic lateral thrusts by rapidly advancing tributaries (Plate 13, B), but in others they seem to be related to intense compressive flow (Plate 14, A). This occurs where the glacier has become much thicker in order to develop a surface slope adequate to carry it across a gentle or reversed reach on its floor. Some of the most spectacular folds of this type yet seen are those of the Malaspina Glacier (Plate 14, B). The Malaspina rests in a basin extending at least 700 and possibly 1000 feet below sea level. Over much and perhaps nearly all of its journey across this basin the ice flows uphill on a floor sloping back toward the mountains. This, plus a high rate of melting, causes it to undergo strong compressive flow. Folding seems to be the principal way in which the glacier responds to these requirements and makes itself thicker. These structures give all appearances of being flow folds, although there is abundant evidence of at least limited slippage on planes parallel to the axes of the folds. The geologist cannot apply his usual fold terminology to these structures as they involve near-vertical morainal septa rather than initially gentle dipping strata. They are better thought of as wave forms with steeply inclined axes.

Ogives

Beautifully curved light and dark bands appearing on the surfaces of some glaciers below icefalls command immediate attention because of their striking symmetry and near periodic repetition (Plate 15). These features are known as ogives, but the term has been applied to such a variety of features that some distinctions are desirable.

First, there are wave ogives which consist of a series of transverse swells and swales on the surface below an icefall. The swells are commonly 200 to 500 feet apart and rise 10 to 20 feet above the adjacent troughs. These features are most prominent near the base of the icefall, become weaker downglacier, and usually disappear completely in less than a mile. In plan view they become convex downglacier owing to the faster flow of the central ice. For years wave ogives have been thought

Plate 13

A—Small tight plunging folds along south margin of Saskatchewan Glacier, Canada. (Photo by M. F. Meier, 28 July, 1952).

B—Deformed moraines in lower reach of Susitna Glacier in the Alaska Range. Much of the major deformation seen here appears to be due to powerful surges of tributary ice streams. (Air photo by Bradford Washburn).

Plate 14

A—Flow folds in lowermost reach of Lowell Glacier where it spills onto flat floor of Alsek River Valley, Yukon Territory, Canada. Late August, 1951.

B—Flow folds within the Malaspina Glacier, Alaska. View looking west-south-westerly across southeastern part of the glacier. August, 1951. A horizontal line across middle of photo would be at least 3 miles long.

Plate 15 —Ogives on surface of lower Austerdals Glacier, Norway. (Photo by R. L. Shreve, 1959).

of as pressure waves related in some way to variations in the compression occurring at the base of an icefall. This may be their origin in some instances, although the cause of a near-periodic variation in compression is not known. Recently, John Nye has shown that pressure cannot account for the wave ogives of the Austerdals Glacier in Norway. He proposes, instead, an ingenious mechanism which involves seasonal variations in melting of ice passing through the icefall. Ice is greatly stretched out in the icefall, so more of it is exposed to summer melting than normal. In addition, the difference between considerable melting in summer and none in winter is accentuated when the summer and winter units of ice are thickened by compressive flow at the base of the fall. The summer units are thin so they underlie the swales, and the winter units are thicker so they underlie the swells. No variation in flow velocity or in compression is required. Under the Nye concept, a swell- and swale-pair constitute an annual feature.

Another kind of ogive is one involving differences in structure or nature of the ice in bands within the glacier. These we shall call internal ogives. They need have no particular topographic expression as contrasted to wave ogives which are solely topographic features. Internal ogives appear on the bare ice tongue below the firn edge as alternate arc-shaped bands of dark and white ice (Plate 15). On some glaciers the dark bands are narrower than the white bands, but this is not universal. Internal ogives are conformable with the arc-shaped foliation, and indeed to a large degree involve a variation in the strength of the foliation.

The only internal ogives we have studied are those of the Blue Glacier, which are not particularly strong (Plate 9, A, p. 50). Close inspection shows that the white bands are underlain by relatively uniform coarse bubbly ice. The dark bands are underlain by strongly foliated, heterogeneous material containing unusually large amounts of fine and coarse-clear ice. The darker color is due principally to a surficial accumulation of fine dark silt. It is not apparent that the ice underlying the dark bands is any dirtier. Its rougher surface may simply trap more silt.

We have proposed the following hypothesis for origin of the Blue Glacier ogives. They are clearly seen only in that part of one ice stream in which large, subequally spaced transverse crevasses or groups of crevasses are formed in the icefall (Plate 9, A). These crevasses become partly or wholly filled by snow, firn, and firn-ice breccia by the time they reach the base of the fall. Here they are subjected to intense compression, and the jumbled mixture of materials filling the crevasses is squeezed, partly recrystallized and greatly modified. The large degree of inhomogeneity is particularly favorable for the formation of strong foliation. These greatly modified crevasse fillings are thought to compose the ogive dark bands seen below the firn edge. The arc shape is developed by differential flow just below the base of the fall. The conformity of foliation and ogives shows that they are formed in about the same place by the same or closely related processes. The site of origin is judged to be the "structural mill" at the base of the icefall where intense compressive flow prevails. The fact that the Blue Glacier ogives disappear within one-half mile below the firn edge indicates that they extend into the ice to an approximate depth of 100 feet, as that is roughly the amount of ice removed from the surface by melting in this distance of travel.

Everyone seems to agree that icefalls are necessary for the formation of ogives of both the surface and internal variety, but not all icefalls generate ogives, at least that are strong enough to be recognized. No definite relationship has yet been firmly established between wave and internal ogive, although some glaciers such as the Austerdals have both. The Nye ablation mechanism appears to be a promising explanation for some wave ogives, but the possibility that others are produced by variations in compressive flow at the base of the icefall cannot be entirely dismissed. A quasi-periodic process is clearly required. Many workers are favorably inclined to the idea that this is dependent in one way or another upon the seasonal variations of an annual cycle. Evidence seems good that some ogives are annual, but it is not yet certain that they all are. Ogives of the Blue Glacier variety, if correctly interpreted, require only a subequal spacing of large crevasses or groups of crevasses in which the breccia insets are formed. There is as yet no evidence that this need involve an annual cycle, although it may.

OXYGEN-ISOTOPE RATIOS

General Statement

Many readers will recall that the atomic weight of oxygen is 16, in chemical practice written O^{16}. Those who have kept up on their chemistry know that there is a heavier stable isotope of oxygen, O^{18}. Most of you will remember that water is H_2O, but you probably do not know that about 0.2 per cent of the oxygen in natural water is O^{18}. Whenever you take a drink of water you introduce a little O^{18} into your system. The work of Epstein, his associates, and others has established beyond doubt that relatively large variations occur in the O^{18}/O^{16} ratio of natural precipitation.

The O^{18}/O^{16} ratio of a specimen is measured in a mass spectrometer, and the practice is to compare it with the ratio of a standard material, commonly average sea water. The deviation of the specimen ratio from the standard ratio, designated as δ, is expressed by the following formula.

$$\delta = \left(\frac{H_2O^{18}/H_2O^{16}\ (\text{specimen})}{H_2O^{18}/H_2O^{16}\ (\text{standard})} - 1 \right) \ x\ 1,000$$

If the ratio of the sample is lighter (less O^{18}) than the ratio of the standard, as it is in all natural precipitation, the δ value is negative.

The potential use of O^{18}/O^{16} ratios in the study of glaciers is based in part on the following points. (1) The δ values for snow, firn, and ice vary over a range far greater than the limitations of accuracy with which they can be measured. (2) The ratios are known to be strongly influenced by the temperature at which precipitation takes place, so they reflect the altitude and the season at which precipitation occurs. (3) The previous history of the air masses from which the precipitation falls is also known to affect the ratios (Fig. 20). Although O^{18}/O^{16} ratios undergo modification and local homogenization once the snow is on the ground, they retain general characteristics related to the site of deposition. Thus, O^{18}/O^{16} ratios can be used as natural tracers within a glacier system to determine the site and season of accumulation and the subsequent history of the materials. The study of O^{18}/O^{16} ratios in glaciers is still in a developing stage. More questions have been raised by the data obtained than answers given. Nevertheless, this looks to be an interesting and promising approach to the investigation of glaciers.

[69]

O^{18}/O^{16} Ratios in Glaciers

To begin with, the O^{18}/O^{16} ratios tell something about the nature of the climatological environment in which a glacier exists. For example, compare the value and range of ratios for the Blue, Saskatchewan, Greenland and Antarctic glaciers as shown in Figure 21. The ratios clearly get more negative (lighter) with increasing latitude and decreasing mean annual temperature. The most negative precipitation yet measured is from the South Pole, which is what theory predicts. The range in values also gives some measure of the variability of the climate, assuming that the sampling is complete, which it is not for all localities plotted in Figure 21. The large range shown for Greenland is almost certainly due to a complete and detailed job of sampling by Carl Benson. The effect of altitude on O^{18}/O^{16} ratios is nicely shown by snow samples from the Blue Glacier as plotted in Figure 22. The ratio becomes more negative at a rate of 1 unit in the δ value for each 650 feet increase in altitude.

The effect of temperature on oxygen-isotope ratios is recorded in snow samples collected during the winter of 1957-58 by a group from the University of Washington working on the northeast slope of Mt. Olympus above the lower Blue Glacier. Analyses of these samples demonstrate that the ratio becomes more negative with colder temper-

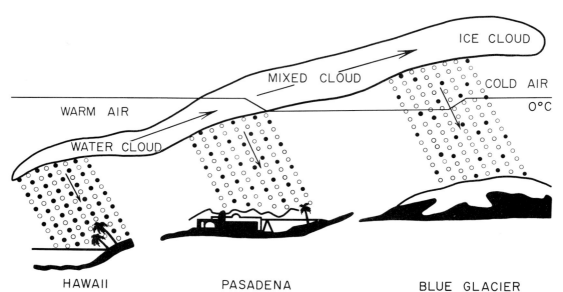

FIGURE 20. Cartoon depicting progressive depletion of O^{18} in sequence of precipitation coming from a single progressively cooling air mass. Open circles represent O^{16}, solid dots represent O^{18}.

atures. This is also seen within the annual layers of accumulated snow and firn where the ratios range from most negative in the winter snow to less negative in both the fall and spring snow. This annual curve of ratio variations can be used independently to identify and define the annual layers of snow. It has been applied most successfully for this purpose in Greenland (Fig. 23) by Epstein and Benson and has made possible identification of annual layers in cores from a depth of 1400 feet in the Greenland Ice Sheet. The O^{18}/O^{16} ratios thus provide a valuable tool for determining rates of accumulation and variations in the climatic environments of large glaciers. Eventually, when more information is available, it may be possible to place approximate temperature values on some of the ratios recorded in glacier materials. This will be a big step forward in the determination of former climatic conditions attending the development of some of our larger and older glaciers.

The oxygen-isotopes show that homogenization and other changes start to occur as soon as the snow is on the ground. They also continue for some time thereafter, perhaps to some degree for the lifetime of the material. Refreezing of downward percolating meltwater is clearly a major cause of homogenization in the accumulation area. Other processes such as vapor transfer, pressure melting and recrystallization may continue the homogenization far down in the ice tongue. This is a matter needing much more study.

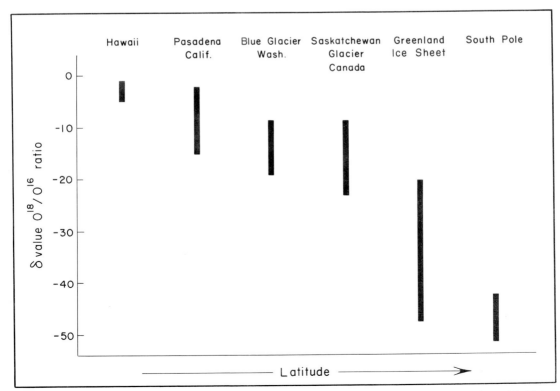

FIGURE 21. Plot showing that O^{18}/O^{16} ratio of precipitation becomes more negative with higher latitude.

Oxygen isotopes can be used to good effect in studying relationships within the ice tongue. For example, ratios of ice samples collected from the firn edge to the terminus show a general trend toward more negative values downglacier on both the Saskatchewan and Blue glaciers. This gives modest support to deductions concerning flowlines in a valley glacier (Fig. 1). The ice toward the terminus should come from the higher part of the accumulation basin, so its ratio should be more negative, as it is.

Analyses of samples taken along profiles across a glacier help identify the source of different ice streams composing the glacier. In the instance of Blue Glacier, the *Gesundheitstrasse* stands out as abnormally heavy (less negative). This is consistent with the concept that it incorporates much snow within and at the foot of the icefall.

We have long debated the origin of lenses and folia of fine ice which are intimately integrated into the foliation pattern of the glacier (Plate 11, A). They may represent original coarse-grained ice that was ground up mechanically during glacier motion or recrystallized into smaller grains by intense stress. The alternative is that the fine ice represents snow or firn incorporated into the glacier by insetting into crevasses or by some other means. If this were the origin of the fine ice, then it should generally have an O^{18}/O^{16} ratio less negative than the closely associated coarse-grained ice. Analyses for the Blue Glacier shows that in 80 per cent of the cases this is the situation. Therefore,

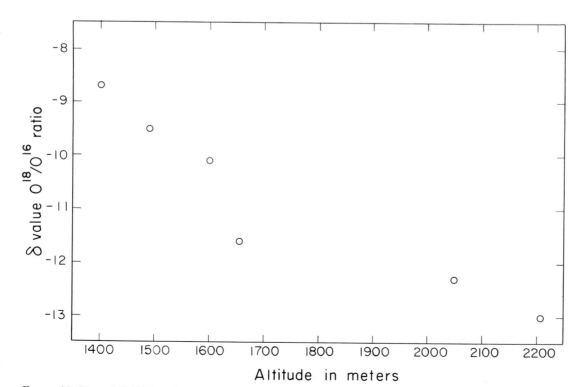

FIGURE 22. Plot of O^{18}/O^{16} ratios in snow from Blue Glacier showing that ratios become more negative with increasing altitude at rate of about 1 unit per 650 feet elavation.

we conclude that most and possibly all fine ice on the Blue Glacier represents inset bodies of snow or firn.

Oxygen isotopes have already proved useful in glacier research. We anticipate that development of a better understanding of the basic relationships controlling oxygen-isotope behaviors will ultimately make them even more valuable as a tool in glacier research.

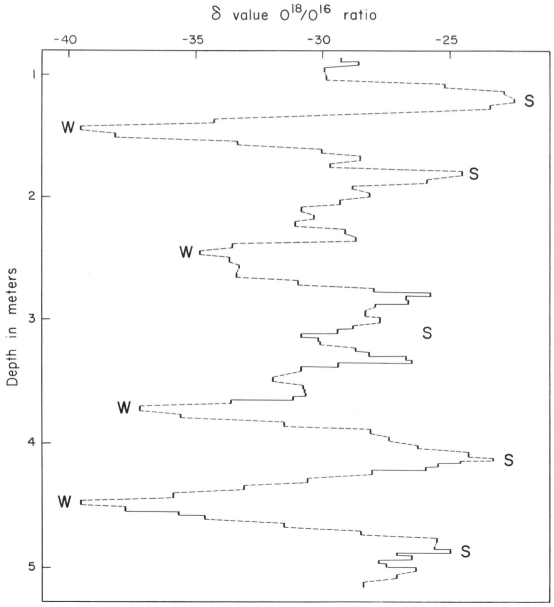

FIGURE 23. Seasonal variations in the O^{18}/O^{16} ratio can be used to identify annual layers in accumulated firn on Greenland Ice Sheet. S=summer layer; W=winter layer, data from Epstein and Benson, on basis of samples supplied by Snow, Ice, Permafrost Research Establishment.

THE FUTURE

The question is often asked, "Will there be another Ice Age"? This query is inspired partly by popularization of a certain hypothesis concerning the cause and control of glaciations and by the fact that glaciers in some local areas, the Pacific Northwest for example, have recently expanded and advanced. When viewed in proper perspective the performance of these particular glaciers is but a minor perturbation within the history of glacier behavior since the last major Ice Age. Insofar as one can tell, the rapid shrinkage experienced by most glaciers during the last one or two centuries may have slowed down, but it has not yet been convincingly demonstrated that the trend has been reversed. Even if it had, this does not necessarily herald the onset of a new glacial age. The glaciers of the world are today more numerous and much larger than they were 4000-5000 years ago.

This is so because of a notable growth and expansion that started about 2500 years ago and extended to about 200 years ago. The history since then has been principally one of rapid shrinkage and recession, interrupted by minor and local episodes of expansion. Since the much larger and more general growth of glaciers 2500 years ago has not as yet led to a new major glacial age, there is no reason to conclude that much smaller upsurges indicate that the North American continent is once again about to be inundated by a large ice sheet. Geological history suggests that such an occurrence is entirely possible, indeed likely, but no hypothesis or present glacier behavior permits anyone to assert with any degree of confidence that the next Ice Age is on its way.

Interest in glaciology, the study of existing glaciers, has run an uneven course. Enthusiasm was high and much excellent work was done in the middle part of the last century and again about the beginning of the present century. In the times between, activities have lagged. Currently we are riding the crest of a wave of high interest in glaciology which has lasted nearly 25 years and shows no signs of slackening. This resurgence began in the mid-1930's with investigations by Ahlmann, Sverdrup, and associates in the North Atlantic region and with research in the Alps by a group of able British scientists guided by Gerald Seligman. During World War II the interest in ice and glaciers was stimulated by operations in far northern regions, and the post-war period saw a considerable upturn in the number, scope and variety of glaciological research projects. Publication of the Journal of Glaciology, starting in 1947 under auspices of the British Glaciological Society has sustained this interest.

Finally, activities of the International Geophysical Year, 1957-1958, and of the subsequent International Geophysical Cooperation, focusing heavily in polar regions, have brought more men into glaciology and expanded activities. Currently the demand for glaciologists far exceeds the supply. This is a highly inter-disciplinary field in which able young men well trained in physics, mathematics, geophysics, geology, meteorology, chemistry and various branches of engineering can make telling contributions. The adventurous scientist will find that opportunities are great, support adequate, and the challenge high.

Like all fields of science, glaciology is an ever-expanding frontier. Each discovery opens up new vistas for research. The more one learns, the more there is to be learned. This is the never-ending challenge that sustains the indomitable spirit of man.

SELECTED REFERENCES FOR
SUPPLEMENTARY READING

General Treatments

Ahlmann, H. W. (1948) *Glaciological research on the North Atlantic Coasts.* Royal Geogr. Soc., Research Series No. 1, 83 pages.

This is a good summary treatment of glaciological investigations in Norway, Iceland, Greenland and Spitsbergen dealing principally with accumulation and wastage, régime, temperature relationships, and some aspects of glacio-meteorology.

Flint, R. F. (1957) *Glacial and Pleistocene geology.* John Wiley and Sons, Inc., New York, 553 pages.

A good comprehensive modern textbook principally on glacial geology and related matters including considerable information on glaciers, present and ancient.

Matthes, F. E. (1942) *Glaciers:* Chap. V in *Physics of the Earth.* Vol. 9, Meinzer, O. E., Editor, McGraw-Hill, p. 149-219.

An excellent review of many aspects of glacier investigations both old and new up to about 1940 by a man who was widely read on the subject and understood it thoroughly.

Those who read German will find the following two books excellent. They are better than anything yet available in English in terms of their coverage of glacier studies.

Hess, Hans (1904) *Die Gletscher.* F. Vieweg and Son, Braunschweig, 426 pages.

Klebelsberg, R. v. (1948) *Handbuch der Gletscherkunde und Glazialgeologie.* Vol. 1, Spring, Vienna, 403 pages.

Glaciers and Climate

This topic is treated to some extent in the general references listed but the following little booklet is also worthy of attention.

Ahlmann, H. W. (1953) *Glacier variations and climatic fluctuations.* Amer. Geogr. Soc., Bowman Memorial Lectures, Series Three, 51 pages.

Glacio-Meteorology

Wallén, C. C. (1948) *Glacial-meteorological investigations on the Kårsa Glacier in Swedish Lapland.* Geografiska Annaler, Vol. 30, p. 451-672.

A comprehensive summary of extended investigations of a small Swedish glacier which incorporates and builds upon the fruits of much of the earlier work in this field.

Orvig, Svenn (1954) *Glacial-meteorological observations on icecaps in Baffin Island.* Geografiska Annaler, Vol. 36, p. 193-318.

This reports a study similar to Wallén's but of more modern date. No single comprehensive summary treating glacio-meteorology in all its aspects has yet been published. These two papers give a good idea of the scope of the field.

Snow and Associated Phenomena

Seligman, Gerald (1936) *Snow structure and ski fields.* Macmillan and Co., Ltd., London, 555 pages.

Although now a little out of date, this book presents in an easily understood manner many interesting aspects of snow and the changes it undergoes after accumulating on the surface.

Gases in Glacier Ice

Nutt, D. C. (1959) *Recent studies of gases in glacier ice, A summary.* Polar Notes, Occasional Publication of the Stefansson Collection, Dartmouth College, p. 57-65.

A good summary of work to date in this as yet little-studied area.

Glacier Flow

Meier, M. F. (1960) *Mode of flow of Saskatchewan Glacier, Alberta, Canada.* U. S. Geological Survey, Professional Paper 351, 70 pages.

The most comprehensive study yet made of a single North American glacier. Also good for structures to be seen in glaciers.

Nye, J. F. (1952) *The mechanics of glacier flow.* Journal of Glaciology, Vol. 2, p. 82-93.

A modern classic of theoretical analysis on modes of glacier flow.

Sharp, R. P. (1954) *Glacier flow: a review.* Geological Society of America, Bull., Vol. 65, p. 821-838.

A review of earlier investigations and thoughts on glacier flow and of structures and other features related thereto.

Melt Figures in Ice Crystals

Nakaya, Ukichiro (1956) *Properties of single crystals of ice, revealed by internal melting.* Snow Ice Permafrost Research Establishment, Reseach Paper 13, 80 pages.

This is by far the best piece of work yet done in this field, beautifully illustrated.

Crystal Orientation in Glaciers

Rigsby, G. P. (1960) *Crystal orientation in glacier and in experimentally deformed ice.* Journal of Glaciology, Vol. 3, p. 589-606.

This paper provides the best description and summary available on work on this subject.